The Youngest Voyageur

Duane R. Lund

Distributed by
Adventure Publications, Inc.
P.O. Box 269
Cambridge, MN 55008

ISBN 0-934860-41-6

The Youngest Voyager

Second Printing, 1993
First Printing, 1985

Printed in the United States of America by

Nordell Graphic Communications, Inc.
Staples, Minnesota 56479

NQ

TABLE OF CONTENTS

INTRODUCTION

THE VOYAGEURS—so great their achievements, so spectacular their endurance, so colorful their attire, so unique their mission—they could have come out of fiction or a modern day adventure video presentation—but they were very much for real.

In the history of man, there has never been a system of trade or transportation quite like it. Few human physical accomplishments can match those achieved by the voyageurs; they demanded as much of their bodies as Olympic athletes. And it was far more than a single venture; their spectacular journeys across the North American continent continued for more than two hundred years.

Our youngest voyageur, Pierre La Vérendrye, is a fictional character, although he is the mythical great-grandson and namesake of a very real hero, Pierre La Vérendrye, the explorer—one of the most significant in the history of our continent. The members of Pierre's immediate family are also fictional, but the men he met, the places he traveled, and the life he experienced are as true to history as the author could relate them. The fact that the book is a work of fiction should not detract in any way from its portrayal of the historic voyageur.

Someone, of course, had to be the youngest voyageur. We don't really know his name or exactly when he lived. We hope his adventures were as exciting as those of our mythical voyageur, and whoever he was, we dedicate this book to him.

CHAPTER I
A NEW HOME

Pierre stood staring out of the kitchen window, absent-mindedly watching the blizzard raging outside. At times he could not see the big pine trees at the edge of the clearing. Three little chickadees, their feathers fluffed for warmth, sat in a bush only inches from his face— partially sheltered by the house against the driving wind. He thought how fortunate he was to be inside the warm cabin, and momentarily stopped feeling sorry for himself.

It was Pierre's fifteenth birthday and just about everything that could go wrong in a young man's life, up to that point, seemed to have happened to this young French Canadian. He had recently arrived in his aunt and uncle's home near Montreal from Three Rivers, Quebec, where he had lived all of his life. He had never known his mother; she had died while giving birth to him. He was the first and only child of Rene' and Francois La Verendrye. His father had been a voyageur who had lost his life in the western wilderness when Pierre was only ten. He had drowned in a nameless rapids somewhere between Lake Superior and the Lake of the Woods. For the past five years, and every summer before that, while his father was in the West, Pierre had lived with his mother's parents. But now they, too, were gone. Last year, his grandfather passed away; he just seemed to have died of old age. And now his grandmother had died of pneumonia. So Pierre had left Three Rivers, and all his friends, to come here to live with his last remaining close relatives, his father's brother, Jean Baptiste, and his wife, Emile. The couple had no children of their own and were genuinely delighted to have Pierre come live with them.

"All's well that ends well." That's what Jean Baptiste had told him again and again.

"It doesn't matter what has happened in the past, it's what happens from now on that's important," his uncle preached.

As the boy stood watching the early December snow obliterate all but the closest images, he felt the big, burly arm of his uncle slip around his shoulder as he whispered in his husky, raspy voice, "Happy Birthday, Pierre."

The youth didn't move and he didn't speak. He had been too deep in thought—depressed about all that had happened and confused about what the future might hold—to say anything.

So Jean Baptiste spoke again, "Cheer up, lad, it's your birthday, it's a time to celebrate! Your whole life is ahead of you. What's happened up to now is all behind you, it's what happens from here on that counts."

Pierre managed a smile as he turned towards his uncle, and said in a voice he hardly recognized as his own because it had suddenly changed and deepened about the time he left Three Rivers, "Yes, I know, like you always say, 'All's well that ends well.'" And then added, as he turned back towards the window, "But I can't help but wonder when things are going to start changing for the better."

Just then Emile's melodious voice interrupted, "Come on you two, time for tea and biscuits."

Pierre absentmindedly walked to the big round kitchen table and pulled out the chair which had been designated as his since the first day he had arrived in his new home, not even noticing the package in front of his place. He automatically lifted the cup of steaming hot tea.

Emile nudged the package closer to her nephew and said, "We were going to save your present for tonight, when you'll have your birthday cake, but I thought you could use some cheering up. Open it."

Pierre stammered his appreciation as he slipped off the red ribbon and removed the brown paper wrapping. Inside was a gift to excite any boy, a handsome hunting knife with a handle made of deer antler. It was cradled in a sheath of heavy moose hide. With a grin from ear to ear, he repeated his thanks, again and again.

Jean Baptiste explained, "I made it myself when I learned you were coming to live with us. I'm glad you like it. Take good care of it and it should last you a lifetime."

"I will, I will, Uncle Jean!" Pierre assured him and, forgetting his tea and biscuits, fingered its sharp blade.

Emile and Jean Baptiste exchanged glances. They were pleased with the boy's response. Perhaps this was the break they had been waiting and hoping for. It was just about the first time he had smiled or spoken with any enthusiasm since he had arrived. They had long wanted a son or daughter of their own but had been unable to have children. Pierre

...a handsome hunting knife with a handle made from a deer antler, cradled in a sheath of heavy moose hide.

was ten when they had last seen him and they were naturally concerned about what it would be like, suddenly having a son, and a teenager at that. But they were more than pleased with the new member of their family. Apart from being so despondent, Pierre was no problem to have around. He always spoke with respect and did everything he was asked, and more.

Although not a tall boy, Pierre was mature for his fifteen years, both in behavior and in appearance. His shoulders were already starting to broaden and he was heavy for his height—an indication he would one day have a build like his father, or uncle for that matter. Jean Baptiste looked as wide as he was tall—particularly at the shoulders and through his deep chest. He had an ideal build for the voyageur that he was. The payload of each canoe was the freight it carried, not the human cargo. Tall, long-legged men took up too much valuable space—nor were their long, lean bodies made for carrying heavy packs on long portages. Jean Baptiste had huge arms, developed by many years of paddling, and a thick bull neck, made strong by supporting a tumpline he used when carrying trade goods or furs over countless wilderness portages. It crossed the forehead and then dropped over his shoulders and down his back, supporting the parcels in the best position for a balanced load.

His curly black hair and dark complexion gave him a swarthy appearance. He almost looked mean, but you liked the man immediately when his broad smile exposed his ivory white teeth, or when he gave forth his hearty laugh, which started somewhere down in his lean belly and gurgled up and out, ending in a hearty roar. When he wasn't smiling or laughing, he was usually singing in a rich baritone, and when he sang, it was nearly always a happy tune. Jean Baptiste La Vérendrye was all man, all French, and all voyageur.

Emile was as feminine as her husband was manly—petite, fine-boned, with soft olive skin, and black eyes that snapped whenever she was laughing, which was often, or when she was angry, which was rare.

It was a good marriage, in spite of the fact that they were apart so much of the time. Jean Baptiste was gone from ice-out to freeze-up, and every third year he was away over the winter, trading on the Lake of the Woods, several hundred miles to the West. During her husband's long absences, Emile went to live with her elderly parents in Montreal itself—a half dozen miles from their wilderness log cabin. The life of a voyageur's wife was not an easy one, and she looked forward to that day when her man would settle down, but she knew that was many years away. Jean Baptiste was a voyageur through and through, and she knew that when she married him.

Pierre, of course, wanted to be a voyageur too, and the sooner the better. In fact, it was his consuming ambition and he dreamed about it day and night. He remembered his father well and his never-ending stories of wilderness adventure; crossing the Great Lakes, paddling on wild rivers, portaging on challenging trails, joining in the wild celebrations at Rendezvous time, trading with the Indians, shooting big game, and exploring where white men had never been. Pierre's home in Three Rivers was also the home of many other voyageurs, and it was the historic launching pad for several famous explorations:

> It was from Three Rivers that missionaries Breboeuf, Lalemant, Le Jeune, and Daniel began their journey which ended in martyrdom at the hands of the Mohawks.
>
> It was from Three Rivers that Joliet and Marquette launched their explorations to the Great Lakes and Minnesota.
>
> It was from Three Rivers that La Salle ventured toward modern day Illinois.
>
> It was from Three Rivers that the story came of young Radisson, a founder of the Hudson's Bay Company, who was carried away by the Iroquois at the age of sixteen, escaped, was recaptured, and was saved from a death of burning at the stake by an old Indian woman.
>
> It was from Three Rivers that De Noyon set forth to build a fort on Rainy River and make his mark in history as the first white man to see the Lake of the Woods.
>
> And it was from Three Rivers that Pierre's great-grandfather, the "original" Pierre La Vérendrye, had set forth with his four sons to explore the west and, in the process, establish seven forts on the frontier.

Little wonder Pierre's chief goal in life was to be a voyageur. In fact, so far as he was concerned, he was ready now. He had been in his last year in the "sisters' school" in Three Rivers at the time of his grandmother's death, and, in his mind, he knew for sure he did not want or need any further education. He had practically grown up in a canoe. As Pierre saw it, all that stood between him and the realization of his goal was his age, and he had been practicing looking older and being able to carry his fair share on the portages. He knew well the requirement that each voyageur had to carry two 90-pound packs on the long treks. He was also well aware that it was not unusual for men to carry three or even more of the heavy parcels at one time, for which they received an extra French dollar per extra pack on the longer portages. He had been practicing before he came to Montreal, but up until now it was tough enough just getting the 90 pounds off the ground, let alone carrying it a mile or even more as would be required on the trail. In coming to live with his Aunt Emile and Uncle Jean, he saw himself getting much closer to his life-goal. After all, his uncle was lead man in a big Montreal canoe and had a great deal of influence with the officials of the North West Company. If anyone could help him become a voyageur, surely it was his uncle Jean.

So it was, later that day after the supper dishes had been put away and Pierre had enjoyed his second piece of birthday cake, that he joined his uncle in front of the huge open fireplace, where roaring flames fought back the chill of the blizzard still raging outside.

"Uncle Jean," Pierre began, "Tell me some voyageur stories."

"Well, let me think," the powerful man replied, "Shall I tell you about the long, hard days when we started paddling before sun-up and kept going until the last rays of daylight were gone? Or should I tell you about the big storms on Lake Superior when we had to fight for our lives to reach a safe harbor? Or maybe you want to hear about the fun times we've had carrying packs of heavy iron kettles and barrels of rum uphill, over the nine mile trek between Grand Portage and Pigeon River? Or how about all those times we were short of food and worked all day on dried peas boiled together with a little bacon fat?"

Before he could go on, Pierre surprised even himself by leaping to his feet, stepping back of his uncle's chair, and putting a playful headlock on the burly Frenchman with his hand over his mouth so that he could not speak.

"You can't scare me, Uncle Jean! I know what you are trying to do. There is no way you will ever talk me out of becoming a voyageur. So tell me about the exciting places you've been, about singing while you're paddling, about dancing at night around the campfire, about the Rendezvous, about the Indian warriors and real chiefs you have met, and about the winters on Lake of the Woods and all the thick venison and moose steaks you stuffed yourself with!"

"Oh, so you want to play rough, eh?" Jean Baptiste teased as he effortlessly broke the boy's hold and pulled him over his shoulder. In a moment the two were rolling and wrestling on the big oval braided rug in front of the fireplace.

"Don't you know I'm a champion wrestler?" the voyageur teased as he let Pierre try hold after hold—none of which he could keep for more than a few seconds. Even when the boy would hold onto one of his Uncle's arms with both of his, he could not control it. It all ended with Jean Baptiste throwing a heavy leg across Pierre's middle and binding both of the boy's arms with his left arm, leaving one hand free to tickle his victim's ribs until Pierre was laughing uncontrollably and begging for mercy.

Emile finally came to the rescue with the broom she had been using at the moment and her husband retreated to his chair in mock terror. But both were inwardly delighted that Pierre was starting to come out of his shell.

When Pierre finally caught his breath, he returned to begging for more "voyageur talk." This time Jean Baptiste responded seriously. "I know you want to be a voyageur, Pierre, and a voyageur you shall be, but all in due time. I've known some lads who started when they were sixteen. In fact, both your father and I did, but that's a year away for you."

"A year and a half you mean!" Pierre blurted out in a manner completely contrary to his normal quiet, respectful behavior. "I can't wait that long! I can paddle as good as any man. And I've been practicing carrying heavy loads. Just look at my muscle!" Pierre pushed up his shirt sleeve and flexed a fairly impressive, developing bicep.

"Oh, you have a good start, all right," Jean Baptiste said kindly as he rose to pour himself another cup of tea. But Pierre jumped between his uncle and the pot, grasped him around the waist and, with much grunting and straining, managed to lift his uncle's feet clear of the floor.

"There!" Pierre exclaimed triumphantly, "And you weigh more than *two* packs."

Jean Baptiste couldn't help but be impressed with his nephew's eagerness and sincerity, and responded with a laugh, "All right, all right, that is pretty good. And I will work with you. I'll help you, I really will, but it will take time. And you must hear me, Pierre, I will not take you until I am sure you are ready. When that time comes, you can bet your buttons there is nothing I would rather do than have you with me."

With that, he threw another log on the fire, poured his tea, filled and lit his clay pipe, and returned to his favorite chair. "Well, let's see," he mused, "So you want a real voyageur story. Well, there was the time your father and I—we were in the same canoe—had just left Rainy Lake and were going down the Rainy River to Lake of the Woods..."

As the story unfolded, Pierre listened spell-bound, hanging on every word, until Emile spoke up at its conclusion, "I think we had better save any other stories for the long winter evenings that lie ahead. If you are going to grow strong, Pierre, you must have your sleep."

That night, as Pierre crawled up into the loft across from the fireplace and snuggled down into the feather tick, he watched the darting flames below and made believe they came from a voyageur campfire hundreds of miles to the west. When drowsiness finally overcame the fifteen-year-old and his eyelids grew too heavy to keep open, he drifted off into dreams filled with wilderness adventure.

CHAPTER II
GETTING READY

Pierre awoke the next morning to the happy, noisy rustle of pots, pans, and dishes as his aunt made breakfast. But as a normal, healthy teenager he did not stir until Emile's second call. Meanwhile, Jean Baptiste snuck around the corner as Pierre was climbing down the ladder. With a roar and one quick swoop, he grabbed the boy from behind, snatched him off the ladder, flung him over his shoulder, and marched triumphantly to the breakfast table—whistling a French marching tune while Pierre screamed, kicked, and helplessly flailed the air all the way.

"Jean Baptiste La Verendrye!" Emile exclaimed, "I believe Pierre will grow up before you do!"

But she could not feign any great displeasure. She was every bit as happy as her husband to have a son, and she was doubly happy to see Pierre actually laughing and enjoying himself.

And was Pierre really happy? You can bet your buttons—as Jean Baptiste would say! In fact, he couldn't remember when or if he had been happier—surely not in the last five years. All of his anxieties and fears about his new home and foster parents were fast disappearing. He knew he was loved, and that was all that really mattered.

Pierre sat down to a bowl of hot oatmeal still giggling, but finally stammered, "That's all right, Uncle Jean, you had better pick on me while you can, because it is just a matter of time until I'll take you down and sit on you and wash your face with snow. And I'll say, 'This is for that time you grabbed me off the ladder to the loft and threw me over your shoulder!'"

Jean Baptiste roared with laughter until his heavy shoulders shook. He too was delighted that Pierre was starting to feel at home and was sufficiently at ease to tease back.

As he ate, Pierre looked out the window and saw that the storm had passed. A bright sun in a cloudless sky, bordered by rainbow-like sun dogs, forecast a cold December day.

"Ah, Pierre," Jean Baptiste spoke, "I see you notice the change in weather. You know what that means. Today we must hit the trapline and dig out our traps before they freeze in."

"Good," was the boy's short reply. He was anxious to get out of the house.

"We will be staying overnight at the spike camp, you know," the Frenchman added, "So before we leave you had better start developing your voyageur muscles by chopping plenty of kindling and carrying in wood for your aunt to burn while we are away."

Pierre assured him that he would, and when breakfast was out of the way, he headed for the wood shelter on the east side of the cabin.

Well before midday, Pierre and Jean Baptiste put on their fur parkas and hats and their moosehide mukluks, slipped their feet into snowshoes, and headed into the forest. Their packs were light; all they carried were a couple of fresh rabbit carcasses for bait, some extra traps, and the food Emile had prepared. Pierre's new knife was on his belt. Jean Baptiste carried his faithful muzzleloader. The year was 1793, but even by that early date, the Montreal area was pretty well trapped out. That is why the voyageurs went hundreds of miles into the western wilderness, hauling trade goods to be exchanged for furs trapped and hunted by the Indians, all to satisfy the European market's appetite for luxury. But there were still enough animals remaining in the Montreal area to make it well worthwhile for Jean Baptiste to trap each winter he was at home—although this income was not enough to live on. Beaver, muskrat, mink, otter, weasel, martin, fisher, lynx, fox, and wolves were all to be found, even though in diminishing numbers.

Even though Pierre had trapped some, he had much to learn and asked a hundred questions as they plodded their way through the soft snow in the wilderness wonderland.

The first set was not hard to find, because a prime red fox was in it, still alive. Jean Baptiste quickly and mercifully dispatched the animal with a club so as not to harm the pelt. The trap was reset, using a piece of rabbit for bait, and blood was scattered on the snow. Jean Baptiste explained, "Animals are intelligent; they depend upon their wits to survive—so we must leave no human scent. That is why I handle the traps with special gloves, and I use them only for that purpose. Last fall I boiled the traps in water flavored with herbs and spices and some fish slime—I learned that from an Indian friend on Lake of the Woods."

The next several sets were empty, but had to be dug out. The trappers had marked these places well so that they could still be found after a heavy snow. Animals do not move during a storm, so it is not surprising that most traps were untouched. However, now that the wind and snow had stopped, all wildlife would be on the move looking for food, and that was another reason it was important to uncover the traps as soon as possible after the weather cleared.

Next they reached a frozen lake where there were several sets for mink and otter along ice heaves and other spots where the animals entered the water under the ice to catch fish and other food. Tiny houses made of twigs, which Jean Baptiste called "cubbies," sheltered the bait, and two traps were set, one on either side, which the animal hopefully would stumble into while it was trying to figure out how to get at the bait. Here the trappers were a little more successful and they left the lake with three mink and two otter in their packs.

Next came a beaver pond which these animals had created the previous summer by damming up a creek, thereby insuring that there would be enough water so that a severely cold winter would not "make ice" so thick that it would block the underwater entrances to their lodges. Knowing the beavers' love for the bark of the popple tree, Jean Baptiste had cut holes in the ice near each lodge and pushed two popple saplings down into the mud bottom with a trap fastened to each. It was important to use a short chain so that the beaver would not be able to pull the trap up into the lodge where it could take its time freeing itself or, that failing, chew off its foot.

When they reached the beaver pond, Jean Baptiste retrieved a long-handled chisel he had stashed nearby and with it, chopped each sapling free. As each was chiseled loose, Pierre checked and reset the traps. The first had been sprung, but was empty. The second had not been touched. But when he tugged on the third, he felt the heavy weight of a drowned beaver and shouted, "I've got one, Uncle Jean!"

Once Pierre had it out of the water, he had to use both hands to lift the animal off the ice so his uncle could appreciate its great size.

The fifth set also produced a beaver, just a little smaller than the first, and the trappers left the pond with packs that were satisfyingly heavier.

The sun had nearly set by the time they reached the spike camp, and along the way, although most traps were empty, they did manage to pick up a fisher, which reminded Pierre of an overgrown mink, and a beautiful lynx with tufted ears and huge, padded feet. Twice during the day they jumped deer from their beds, but Jean Baptiste did not try to shoot them. There were still a couple of quarters hanging at home and besides, Jean Baptiste planned to save the delicious beaver meat, and that, plus the pelts, would be enough to carry home through the powdery snow.

The spike camp was a very small log cabin, just big enough for two men to find shelter from the cold and rest from their labors. A stone fireplace provided the heat and also served as a place to cook. Thick, springy spruce bows, piled on the floor, made a comfortable bed. Wolf and bear hides covered the spruce and also served as blankets. But before the trappers could think of sleep, the animals had to be skinned. A pot of stew was set over a cheerful fire while they worked as a team, Pierre using his new knife. He was careful to speak several times about its fine quality, with comments like, "This blade sure holds an edge... the handle fits my hand just right...a good knife sure makes skinning easy work."

Jean Baptiste was pleased.

The long day in the woods, a stomach full of venison stew, and the warm fire made Pierre very sleepy, but he fought drowsiness and would not let on that he was tired for fear his uncle would think he was not ready to be a voyageur.

When the supper utensils had been rubbed clean with snow, and after Pierre had meticulously cleaned his knife and put it away, he was relieved to hear his uncle say, "Well, let's turn in. It's another big day tomorrow."

Pierre casually responded, "Well, all right—if you're tired..."

Pierre was the first to fall asleep, but not before listening to a pack of timber wolves howl melodiously at the moon. When another pack answered in the opposite direction, it gave him goose bumps. He dozed off wondering if the wolves were talking about the pair of intruding trappers.

Morning came all too soon. Only a few embers remained of the once roaring fire, even though Jean Baptiste had thrown on a couple logs during the night while still remaining in his bed. It was very cold in the little cabin. Pierre really hated to get up but he was getting chilled, and the thought occurred to him that he could really impress his uncle by rising first and rekindling the fire. Mustering all his courage, he did just that. When the fire was roaring and Jean Baptiste still had not stirred, Pierre let out a war whoop and jumped with all his 140 pounds on top of his sleeping uncle, whose only response was, "Did I just feel a leaf fall on me? Or was it a feather?"

Pierre snorted, "Huh, are you going to sleep all day? You must be getting too old to be a trapper, let alone a voyageur!"

That did it. Jean Baptiste grabbed the boy in a bear hug, growling like a grizzly all the while, and squeezed until Pierre begged for mercy. All the scuffling made the blood flow and soon both were ready to take on another day—starting with a breakfast of hot cereal and chunks of Emile's rye bread, toasted over the fire.

On the return trip to the cabin, three more mink, a martin, an otter, one more beaver and another fisher added to the weight of their packs. Jean Baptiste explained that a fisher is one of the very few animals that will take on a porcupine and win. He pointed out several old quills embedded under the animal's lower jaw in the loose skin of its neck, where they had lodged rather harmlessly.

The return trip took all day, and when the cabin finally came into view, with the smoke curling lazily skyward from its stone chimney, it was indeed a welcome sight, even for Jean Baptiste. Emile had a huge moose roast ready for her men, and they had no trouble disposing of all of it.

Before turning in, Jean Baptiste announced, "Pierre, tomorrow we have a day off from trapping, so we'll begin your training to become a voyageur," and then teased, "That is, if you are not worn out from our little walk in the woods!"

Pierre laughed and responded, "We'll see who wears out who tomorrow!"

The next day Jean Baptiste was as good as his word, and so the training began. No Olympic athlete ever went through a more rigorous preparation. But first the voyageur explained many things to his nephew; from how to lift heavy weights without injuring one's back to how to fall with a pack on your shoulders without getting hurt.

"Your biggest challenge," Jean Baptiste told him, "will be building up enough strength to carry the heavy packs on the portages. It is difficult enough just carrying the load, but some of the portages are through swampy, muddy lowlands, and in other places the scraggly bushes seem to reach out and trip you."

"It wouldn't be so bad," he went on, "if it were all level ground, but in many places you will have to climb sizable hills and then go down steep trails to the next lake. Going downhill with a heavy load on your back can be more difficult than climbing. It is so easy to lose your balance."

Jean Baptiste made up a pack weighing about fifty pounds and told Pierre, "I think this is plenty to start with. Once you've learned to balance this load and have gained some strength, we will gradually increase the weight to 90 pounds, the usual weight of a voyageur's pack.

But remember, a true voyageur carries at least two of these packs!"

Jean Baptiste tied the pack into a tumpline about four inches wide. The band went across Pierre's forehead and then back over his shoulders.

"For a single pack," the teacher explained, "we will tie the parcel short so that the weight rests more on your shoulders than on your back."

"Balance is critical," he added, "if the weight is distributed just right you should be able to lean forward, using your forehead to balance the load as well as carry part of the pressure. If it is positioned right, you should find it easier to trot than to walk. So put on your mackinaw, Pierre, and we'll go outside for a trial run."

After the two of them had shoveled a path about 100 feet long, Jean Baptiste showed his nephew the proper form and ran back and forth as though the pack were not even there.

"Now it's your turn, little voyageur." he said, and proceeded to transfer the pack to the boy's shoulders.

Pierre took about ten steps, lost his balance, and fell face down into the snowbank! Jean Baptiste knew when to tease and when not to tease, as he helped the boy to his feet and readjusted the pack with the assurance, "That's not the last time you'll do that! Don't worry, it will come with practice. I know you can do it."

Pierre smiled an acknowledgement. He was too embarrassed to say anything. But the voyageur knew his business and before long Pierre could trot the entire length of the path and back without losing his balance or having to stop to catch his breath.

After a half hour or so, Jean Baptiste announced, "That is enough for now. Many short practices are better than a few long ones. Just so you work out every day is what counts."

Pierre didn't argue; he was more than ready to go in.

Once inside, the voyageur had more advice: "It is not only important that you develop strong neck, shoulder, back, and leg muscles, but you must also develop stamina. You might start running every day now on snowshoes, and once the snow melts, you should continue to run every day—long distances—at least two or three miles. This will build your wind. It is one thing to lift heavy weights; it is quite another to carry them over a long portage."

Pierre proved to be an excellent student and followed his uncle's suggestions religiously. Before long the 50-pound pack was replaced by one that weighed 60 pounds, then 75, and, finally, a full 90 pounds. Pierre looked in the mirror every day to see if he could detect any muscular development. He even marked out a heavy cord into inches and checked his neck, chest, biceps and calves. Although change came slowly, there was improvement. Much of it was probably due to natural growth, but Pierre gave full credit to working out.

Not too long after he began his training program, on a day off between trap runs, Pierre said to his uncle, "You know, Uncle Jean, I've thought of another way to build up my strength and endurance. I know you are a champion wrestler. Couldn't I build myself up and learn to wrestle at the same time?"

"Now that's an excellent idea!" was Jean Baptiste's quick reply. "Wrestling is the king of sports, and one of the oldest, you know. It goes way back to the Greeks, Romans, and Egyptians. And it is one of the healthiest of sports; you exercise every muscle in your body. Besides, it will be good for me to work out too, lest I grow fat on your aunt's good cooking!"

And with that, and Emile's good natured tolerance, the big oval braided rug in front of the fireplace became a wrestling mat where workouts took place every day they were home from trapping—sometimes by the hour.

Jean Baptiste was indeed a champion wrestler and had earned the title by competing with scores of other voyageurs during the less eventful winter months in the wilderness and at Rendezvous time. He also proved to be a good coach with all kinds of advice for his young student:

> "Never sit on your opponent; your center of gravity is too high and all he has to do is push up on both your knees and you'll go sprawling over backwards."

> "When you get your man down, put your full weight on his chest, pushing with your toes, lifting your head, and arching your back. But keep your body perpendicular to your opponent so that he cannot roll you over."

> "Control your opponent's head and you control him."

> "Move fast; be quick."

> "Work on your balance."

> "Take your man down by lifting one or both of his legs off the ground and driving into him."

> "Use your legs; lock them like a scissors around his stomach and turn your knees into his belly as you squeeze—pulling up with your arms under one or both of his armpits."

"If he's on his stomach, turn him over by working your hand under his arm and then behind his neck. Push down on his neck and lift up under his armpit—turning him over onto his back."

"Believe in yourself. Have confidence that you can handle him. Or if you really aren't sure, make it look as though you are sure. Beat a man's **mind** first, then his body. Look strong; flex your muscles. Tell him you're going to massacre him! Then back up your words and appearance by being aggressive—always take the offensive."

Pierre enjoyed the workouts. Even though he was well over 140 pounds by spring, he was hardly a challenge to his powerful and skilled uncle. This didn't bother him, but he did wonder how he would do against someone his own age, and was looking forward with confidence to the first opportunity he would have to find out.

As winter began to give way to signs of spring, Pierre begged his uncle, almost to the point of being a pest, to let him go along when the voyageurs headed west at ice-out. "I'll carry my fair share. I'm a good paddler. I promise I won't get in the way. I'll do everything you ask me to!"

Jean Baptiste, kindly, but firmly insisted Pierre was simply too young. "There never has been a 15-year-old voyageur," he pointed out again and again.

"Besides," he added, "this year I must go on to Lake of the Woods and stay over the winter."

"All the better," was Pierre's reply, "And I'll do everything you ask and more; I'll run errands; I'll mend your clothes; I'll..."

"Whoa!" Jean Baptiste interrupted, *"Not this year!"*

"But then I'll have to wait two years!" Pierre argued.

"No—if you keep on working out faithfully, I'll arrange for you to meet me at Grand Portage at the Rendezvous and then you can return to Montreal with me a year from this summer."

Pierre was heartbroken. But fate sometimes has a way of intervening, and this time fate was on the boy's side. About the time the snow was all gone and the ice had started to soften along the river's edge, news came that Emile's mother had fallen on a slippery, snow-covered path and broken her hip. Emile confessed to her husband, out of earshot of Pierre, that it might be a problem having him around while nursing her mother back to health. She was concerned, too, how her elderly parents would react to having a restless teenager around the house.

Jean Baptiste knew he would miss the boy and really wanted to have him along, but as lead man in the big Montreal canoe, he didn't want to cause any undue burden for his men. It happened, however, a few days later when he was meeting with his crew and the others who would be traveling together, that he learned one of his regulars had become seriously ill and would not be able to make the run. Fate had intervened on Pierre's behalf once again!

With more than a little hesitation, Jean Baptiste talked first to his crew and then to his superiors. The fact he received no objection from either was a tribute to Jean Baptiste and the high esteem in which he was held. The crew assured him they would pick up any slack and when he promised the company officials he would carry a third pack on portages without extra pay, since Pierre could carry only one, he was told, "No problem."

There was another matter, however, of which Pierre was totally unaware. And one day, Jean Baptiste cautiously asked his wife, "Do you think the boy will be able to handle what he will surely learn about his father when he reaches the Lake of the Woods?"

"Well," Emile replied, "He has to learn sooner or later, but you had better tell any of the men, who knew Francois, to keep still so that he learns it first from you. In fact, why not tell him now?"

"All in due time; all in due time," was Jean Baptiste's philosophical reply—putting off the inevitable.

And so it was that Jean Baptiste looked across the supper table at his nephew one evening and teased with a straight face, "I am pleased, Pierre, that you haven't pestered me about becoming a voyageur for quite some time now; I'm glad that you have apparently come to your senses and are willing to wait a year or so."

Pierre didn't know quite how to respond, but finally muttered, "Really, Uncle Jean, to be honest, I want to go as much as ever, but you and Aunt Emile have been so good to me that I'm a little ashamed of the way I have behaved. I just don't want to make either of you mad at me."

"Well," the Frenchman said, dragging on his clay pipe, "Why don't you ask just once more for good luck?"

Pierre didn't know if he had heard right or, if he had, what his uncle really meant. But he finally stuttered, "Can I—that is—uh—can I go with you—*this* year?"

"Surely, why not?" Jean Baptiste replied casually and without a smile, as he turned to look out the window at the setting sun.

Pierre turned to his aunt for help. "Does he really mean it? He isn't teasing me, is he?"

"Yes, dear, he does mean it. No, dear, he isn't teasing this time." Emile assured him with a smile. "We've talked it over and your uncle has the permission of the crew and the North West Company officials."

Pierre dragged the now laughing Jean Baptiste out of his chair and onto the big oval rug. This time the man let the boy win the wrestling match—just to make his day complete.

CHAPTER III
THE YOUNGEST VOYAGEUR

Two days later, Emile left the wilderness cabin to be with her parents so she could care for her injured mother. Jean Baptiste and Pierre accompanied her on the five mile trek, helping carry the things she would need. She knew she would see her two men again before they started west, so she used this opportunity to lecture them about chores which had to be completed before the cabin was abandoned for the year and a half they would be away. She concluded with, "See if you can't leave everything just as I left it this morning, and don't break any of the furniture with your crazy wrestling matches!"

But there was little time for wrestling. The snow was nearly gone and it looked like there would be an early ice-out. Besides completing Emile's assignments for closing up the cabin, there were so many things to do to get ready for the long journey. Packing their personal things, however, was a small matter because space in the canoe was so limited and they were allowed to bring very little. En route on the warm summer days they would wear little more than a loin cloth. But since they would be staying in the northern wilderness over the winter, when temperatures would plunge to 30° below zero and worse, they would need their deer skin underwear, heavy stockings, mukluks for their feet, wool shirts, trousers, and mackinaw jackets. They would, of course, be living by a trading post and could secure there those other items they might need in the wilderness.

Pierre and Jean Baptiste spent most of their daylight hours on the banks of the St. Lawrence River where the crews of men were making final preparations. Literally every inch of the 40-foot-long voyageur canoes was examined to make certain the crafts were seaworthy. The lives of the men and the safety of the cargo depended on that inspection. Every flaw was corrected and then repair materials were stashed in each canoe: rolls of birch bark, wattape (spruce and cedar roots

which would serve as twine for lacing the pieces of bark together),
spruce gum to seal the cracks, glue made from the spinal column of the
sturgeon, and a few pieces of cedar to be used for patching the frame-
work should that become necessary.

New paddles were fashioned out of birch and other light hardwoods
which would not break easily when used to push the canoes away from
the rocks in the many rapids they would have to negotiate. Most paddles were about three and one-half feet in length and about three or four
inches wide, but a few were half again as long. These were used in the
stern for steering, or in the prow for holding the canoe off the rocks.
The bark canoes were so fragile the voyageurs didn't even dare move
their feet for fear of opening a seam, and a brush against a rock could
be disastrous.

The flamboyant voyageurs, with their love for color, decorated
everything. The paddles of Jean Baptiste's canoe were a bright red.
The rim of the canoe was painted alternately red and green. On both
sides of the bow and stern were painted blue silhouettes of the profile of
the head of an Indian chief. When the work on the canoe was completed, a red feather would be implanted in the stern and another on the
bow to signify that the vessel was seaworthy.

Trade goods and supplies, including axe heads, awls, knives, cloth,
blankets, trinkets (beads and jewelry), basic tools, dried food, and a
variety of items required by the traders for use at the outposts were
packed in canvas bales for protection and for easier carrying on the
portages. The packs were tied so that there were two "ears," one in
each corner at the top of the pack, to serve as "handles" when loading
or unloading the canoes. Heavy iron kettles of a variety of sizes were
"nested," one inside the other, to take up less space. Rum, wine, shot,
and gun powder came by the barrel, and muzzleloaders were protected
by canvas wrappings.

Pierre was, of course, inexperienced in all this, but his quick legs
made him useful as they carried him on scores of errands every day.
Everyone seemed to be his boss:

"Get this, Pierre."
"Get that, Pierre."
"Hold this, Pierre."
"Lift that, Pierre."
"Go find Henri, Pierre."
"Get me a drink, Pierre."
And on and on!

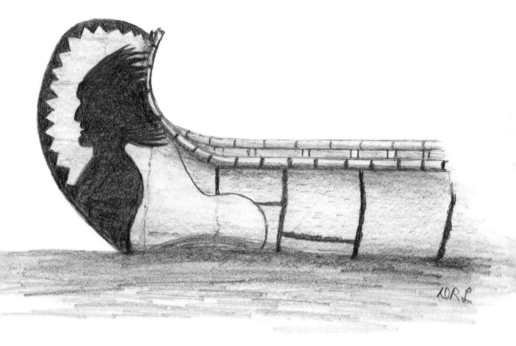

...on both sides of the bow and stern were painted blue silhouettes of the profile of the head of an Indian chief.

As the men worked, they frequently broke into song. One that Pierre especially liked was, "Mon conot d'e'corce"—in honor of the canoe:

"You are my voyageur companion,
I'll gladly die in my canoe,
And on the grave beside the trench
You'll overturn my canoe.

The cart is loved by the farmer,
the hunter loves his dog;
The musician loves his music,
but it is to my canoe I'm bound."

Meanwhile, the boy had a hundred questions, but most went unanswered because everyone was too busy to take the time to explain or answer. So he saved them for Jean Baptiste on the way home each day. Sometimes the uncle wasn't sure which exhausted him more, the hard day's work or his nephew's endless questions.

"What do we do if our canoe breaks up?"

"We build a new one on the spot!"

"Won't that take a long time?"

"Oh, about three or four days if the birch trees are handy."

"What if we lose our load?"

"Then we lose most of our pay!"

"Will we really start before sunup each day and paddle until after dark?"

"With this early break-up we'll have more days to get to Grand Portage, so luckily for you, we should be able to get by with shorter days. And from Grand Portage to Lake of the Woods is nowhere near as far as the first part of our journey, so we shouldn't have to paddle after dark."

"How far can a canoe travel when they start before daylight and paddle 'til after dark?"

"Well, Pierre, I once heard of a canoe that traveled 79 miles in one day on Lake Superior. Somebody figured out that meant 57,600 paddle strokes!"

And on and on and on.

It wasn't as though Pierre was not already quite knowledgeable about what lay ahead. After all, he had dreamed for years of being a voyageur and had asked a thousand questions before this, the answers to which were well imprinted in his keen mind. He knew, for example, that the Montreal canoe which would carry them across the Great Lakes to

Grand Portage on the west end of Lake Superior would have a crew of ten or twelve. The "gouvernail," or steersman, would stand in the stern of the canoe and keep the canoe on course with his long, wide paddle. The "avant de canot," or captain, would be in the prow and responsible for spotting hazards such as reefs or logs and for using his paddle to keep the vessel away from danger. The rest of the crew were called "milieu," or middlemen. The canoe weighed about 500 pounds and would carry a cargo of from 5,000 to 6,000 pounds.

He knew too that the voyageurs who spent their winters in the East were nicknamed "mangeur de lard," meaning, "pork eaters"—partly because the mainstay of their diet was lyed corn or peas boiled in a kettle of water with a few spoons of melted pork fat added to diffuse the kernels and make a stew the consistency of pudding, and partly because during the long winter months back east they occasionally enjoyed domestic meats (such as pork), while their counterparts out West had to live entirely on wild game and fish. The men of the West were called by several names: "men of the north," "Nor'westers," and "hivernauts" (winterers).

Pierre was also well aware that the many long and difficult portages west of Lake Superior meant the heavy Montreal canoes would have to be exchanged for the lighter (about 300 pounds) "north" canoes. They would carry a crew of six or eight and a load of about 3,000 pounds.

The crews would also change. Only he and Jean Baptiste from their canoe would be going on to Lake of the Woods. Some of the others would stop at Rainy Lake, and the rest would return to Montreal with the furs the Nor'westers had brought from the wilderness outposts, from places that would one day be known as "Ontario," "Manitoba," "Wisconsin," "Minnesota," "Illinois," the "Dakotas," and "Saskatchewan." A few would come from as far north and west as Lake Athabasca. It was not possible to make the trip from there to Grand Portage and back before freeze-up. So these super voyageurs were, even now, spending the winter on Rainy Lake at "Athabasca House," having paddled that far last summer. They were waiting for select crews of pork eaters who would bring trade goods to them for their own Rendezvous, after which they would return to Lake Athabasca, hopefully by freeze-up.

And then there was the Rendezvous itself, with all the excitement, color, and atmosphere of a carnival. The voyageurs from east and west would meet at Grand Portage, on the western end of Lake Superior, where trade goods from Montreal merchants would be exchanged for furs from the West. Pierre had heard many stories of the contests, gambling, fighting, drinking, and frolicking that went on there, as the disciplined, hard working voyageurs were permitted to really "let go."

He knew too of the rivalry among the fur trading companies. Pierre and his uncle were employees of the North West Company. Although Canadian born, nearly all of their fellow workers were also of French origin. The company's chief rival was the Hudson's Bay Company, headquartered at York Factory on the bay from which it took its name. It was chartered by the English as a private company, but was originally founded by two Frenchmen, Radisson and Groseilliers, in 1670. Although the country had been under English rule since 1763, the two companies not only competed for furs, but often behaved as though the French and English were still at war. They often played dirty tricks on each other and occasionally got into fights or even burned down the other's trading posts. Then there was the smaller X Y Company, which had splintered off from the North West Company and competed with both.

The great day of departure finally came. It was a beautiful day, as though provided by God just for this special occasion in Pierre's life. The sky was a spotless blue, washed by the previous night's rain. The sun shown warmly and brightly, and the air was saturated with the smells of spring. Migrating birds, particularly ducks and geese, were moving north and their honking and quacking, along with the warbling of the redwing blackbirds, gave the day a festive air.

The voyageurs were dressed in their finest for the occasion; the next day they would change to their older, and less spectacular, work outfits. Emile had made sure Pierre was clothed like all the rest. She had sewn his outfit hurriedly, but well, in the short time since it had been decided he would be going along with Jean Baptiste. Pierre was all decked out in a red shirt, a buckskin vest, leather leggings over blue trousers, moosehide mukluks, a green sash around his waist, and perched on his head was a red and white striped stocking cap with a blue tassel and raven feather dyed red. Some of the voyageurs had real ostrich feathers, imported from Africa, in their caps, and Pierre was determined to trade for one at his first opportunity.

It was very difficult for Emile to say her goodbyes, but she put on a brave front. Life was tough on the frontier, and under that warm, soft exterior, Emile was tough, too. This parting was particularly difficult for her, however, knowing it would be nearly a year and a half before she and Jean Baptiste would be reunited—and it wasn't easy for him either.

As they embraced, she whispered in his ear, "And don't you even dare think of doing what your brother did."

Jean Baptiste whispered back, "Not on your life; now don't you worry."

When it was Pierre's turn for a hug, Emile also gave him a kiss, which really didn't embarrass him because Frenchmen were kissing all the time anyway, and instructed him, "Now take good care of your uncle!"

There was one last stop, at Saint Anne's Church on the western point of Montreal Island, where most voyageurs made a contribution and asked the blessings of their patron saint on their journey.

Then they were finally on their way, up the St. Lawrence to the Ottawa River, joyfully singing "Alouette," as their paddles marked time.

There were eight canoes in this particular flotilla, and Jean Baptiste's canoe led the way. Pierre was so excited he could hardly stand it. He was now truly a voyageur, and the youngest voyageur at that.

CHAPTER IV
ON TO THE
RENDEZVOUS

As the canoes headed west, everything seemed new and exciting to Pierre. They rarely encountered other humans along the river. Everything was wilderness, except for an occasional Indian village, the then small town of Ottawa, and a few trappers bringing their furs to market. The singing of the voyageurs didn't seem to frighten the wildlife. In fact, the loons joined in! Migrating birds were everywhere; ducks, geese, pigeons, and an enormous variety of songbirds. Big game animals were without fear and appeared to be showing off their young; sow bears with their fuzzy cubs, cow moose with their gangly, long-legged calves, and doe deer with their tiny, spotted fawns. All came to the water's edge to drink. Animals whose furs were marketable were more scarce, having already been trapped out along the rivers, but occasionally Pierre would spot a swimming beaver dragging a green branch across the surface of the water to its lodge, or see a mink pulling a flopping fish up onto the shore. Sometimes the ever-curious otter would pop their heads out of the water close to the canoe. Their necks were so long and heads so relatively small they reminded Pierre of pictures he had seen of the cobra snakes of India. The woodland scenery was also very special. The new, tiny, bright green aspen and birch leaves stood out in sharp contrast to the dark green needles of the spruce, balsam, and pine. Big red maple buds, about to pop, added still more color. It was a good time to be alive.

Pierre sat on a narrow seat near the stern of the canoe, just in front of his uncle. Jean Baptiste had chosen to serve as "steersman" until the canoe neared rapids. Then, as captain, he would move to the bow. His position in the rear gave Pierre a good view of his fellow crewmen. Pierre watched with envy the rippling muscles of their backs, shoulders, and arms as they mechanically dug their paddles into the clear water at about 40 strokes a minute. He looked down at his skinny arms and hairless chest and felt puny by comparison. He couldn't help but wonder what these broad-shouldered men of muscle really thought about having a kid along. He had boasted to his uncle just a few months earlier that he could paddle with the best of men. But now, when he had to rest occasionally and miss a few strokes, he was glad the men were in front and couldn't see. If there was any concern, no one showed it. After all, they had their chance to object when Jean Baptiste asked their permission to bring Pierre along as a crew member. The boy could take consolation in the fact that two Montreal businessmen, who were traveling in the third canoe, didn't paddle at all. They were on their way to Grand Portage to help out in the Great Hall. The businessmen were poorly dressed for the wilderness journey with their fancy hats and shirts trimmed with lace. Frontier clothing was apparently below their dignity.

But the voyageurs—now they were Pierre's kind of men, and he had ample opportunity to study each one in his canoe. There was Jacque, who sported a full beard and always had a twinkle in his eye. And Henri, who was nearly bald and sang with the deepest bass voice. Maurice was the youngest of the group but already married, so Pierre couldn't think of him as really being young. Francois was a big tease, but in a nice sort of way, and Pierre liked him a lot. Claude was always laughing, not a hearty laugh like Jean Baptiste, but more of a chuckle that was very contagious. Phillipe was the quiet one. He had a mean-looking scar clear across his forehead, but he really wasn't mean. He just didn't talk much. One night by the campfire, Pierre dared to ask Phillipe how he got his scar. Without facial expression and hardly moving his lips, he replied, "An Indian tried to scalp me, but I got him first, killed him dead, used my knife."

Pierre stayed away from him the rest of the trip. But before they parted company at Grand Portage, Phillipe said to Pierre, "About my scalp wound, I don't want you to be afraid of every Indian you meet. It was just a cut I got from a rock when our canoe dumped me into a rapids. I was just joshin' you."

For the first time Pierre saw Phillipe smile just a little bit. Pierre smiled back, but couldn't think of anything to say, except, "Oh."

Charles seemed to be the oldest. His hair was thin and his skin was leathery, well weathered by many years in the out-of-doors. Then there was Robespiene, whose face looked like it had been pressed in a vice. But all were men, real men, and Pierre felt honored to be among them.

Jean Baptiste's position, right behind Pierre, was handy for conversation and questions, and our young voyageur never seemed to run out of either:

"How big will the waves be on the Great Lakes?"

"Will we ever go out of sight of the shore?"

"Are there really sea monsters in Lake Superior?"

Whenever Jean Baptiste grew weary of the questions, he would just burst into song and the men would pick up the chant. No wonder Pierre concluded his uncle would rather sing than talk!

Their route took them up the Ottawa River, then the Mattawa to Trout Lake, then portaging into Lake Nipissing and down the French River. There were eighteen portages to where the Mattawa joined the Ottawa, and as many "discharges" (less dangerous, shallow rapids, where the canoes were partially unloaded so they could float safely through). "Sitting poles" were used in the shallows instead of paddles.

Before entering the Mattawa, Jean Baptiste stopped the canoe and the men rested their paddles as they breathed a prayer of thanksgiving for their safe travel thus far, a custom observed by all voyageurs. Pierre never did get used to seeing the little white crosses along the way, each marking the death and/or grave of a voyageur. As each cross was encountered, the voyageurs respectfully doffed their caps. Once they entered Lake Nipissing, the sitting poles were no longer needed, and they were thrown away with a shout of celebration.

When the canoes finally did leave the rivers and smaller lakes behind and moved out onto Lake Huron, Pierre was impressed. For the first time in his life, he looked out across water where he could not see the other side. A light west wind greeted them. One day when the wind changed to the east, Pierre observed, "It's nice to have the wind to our backs now we can use the sail."

But Jean Baptiste grunted, "No good. East wind means a storm soon."

As usual, Jean Baptiste was right. Fortunately it came in the middle of the night. The men had been careful to take precautions and had sought out a sheltering cove with a pebbly beach. As the storm hit, they crawled under the turned over canoes and kept relatively dry. Pierre slept little. With the flashing of lightning, crashing of thunder, and loud snoring of the voyageurs reverberating under the canoe, it was little wonder!

The next morning, the men paused off shore to throw tobacco on the water. "A peace offering," Jean Baptiste explained. "It is to pacify Vielle, the old woman of the wind."

Softly, each voyageur uttered the words, "Souffle, souffle, la Vielle," (Blow, blow, old woman).

When the canoe reached Sault Ste. Marie, it was an excuse for a day of rest. Jean Baptiste was busy visiting old friends. He seemed to know everyone, and Pierre just explored. He was especially interested in watching the trading already taking place. Trappers from points south and other nearby outposts were exchanging furs for trade goods. Pierre was particularly intrigued with the fur press, a machine that squashed the pelts into smaller bundles so they would take up less space in the canoes as they headed for Montreal and points east.

Lake Superior was the last huge body of water, and it proved to be the least friendly. Gusty winds churned up huge waves with whitecaps. These "swells," as Jean Baptiste called them, lifted the canoe so high Pierre felt as though he could see forever. But when the boat dropped down into the trough, all he could see was water. Paddling was like going up a hill, then down a hill. Jean Baptiste's skillful steering kept the spray to a minimum, but several times during each day, the voyageurs took turns bailing with huge sponges while the rest kept the canoe moving and on course. When the wind switched to the northwest, the canoes hugged the shoreline and the going was much better.

There was a brief stop at Fort Kaministiquia, where a river by that name divided into three parts and then spilled into Lake Superior. Jean Baptiste told him that his great grandfather and namesake, Pierre La Vérendrye the explorer, had spent the first winter here on his first trip West. Pierre would live to see the day when this fort and the route up the Kaministiquia River would be busier than Grand Portage and the Pigeon River way, once it was discovered (about 1800) that Grand Portage was on American soil and customs would have to be paid on all goods entering the United States at that point, even though their eventual destination was in Canada. The Kaministiquia post would become known as "Fort William."

The last day on Lake Superior, there was no wind at all. Even so, Pierre could feel the dying swells as the canoe gently rose and fell. In the calm water, Pierre was entranced with how far down he could see into the clear depths, whenever the voyageurs rested from their paddling to enjoy their pipes. He sometimes saw huge fish, which the men identified as lake trout.

When they drew close to Grand Portage, all eight canoes went ashore so the men could put on their dress outfits. They wanted to look their best when they saw their friends. Then, swinging around the last point between Mutton Island and the mainland, they picked up their favorite chanty, "At the Clear Running Fountain," and sang at the tops of their voices as they sped for shore. Pierre never forgot the sight as the huge stockade came into view with Mt. Rose in the background. The panorama was more than he had expected. Protruding above the walls of the stockade was the Great Hall, where most of the business transactions took place. There were many other buildings within the stockade. Pierre later counted sixteen in all. They were painted a rich brown and had shingled roofs. He couldn't believe how many people were there, way out in the wilderness. Coming down the portage trail, behind the fort, were dozens of Nor'west voyageurs with their packs of furs. Other canoes from the East were still being unloaded of their trade goods on the shore. There were tents and wigwams everywhere. The tents pitched up the hill to the left in back of the fort, he learned later, belonged to the men from the North and West. The pork eaters, on the other hand, slept under their canoes when it rained. A small brook separated the encampments. There were several hundred voyageurs already there and even more Indians. Canoes were scattered everywhere, some under construction and others being repaired. The Indians had a regular canoe factory going. Pierre learned later they made about 70 canoes here each year for sale to the trading companies. It was a beehive of activity.

Pierre was amazed to see several cows grazing on the edge of the forest and a pen full of hogs. Jean Baptiste explained that the cows provided milk for the traders and other permanent employees at the post and that the pigs were used for special feasts.

As the voyageurs in each canoe finished unloading their vessel and carrying the trade goods to the appointed place, they were free to do whatever they wished. At first, most were just visiting or resting, but as the day wore on, there were some more-or-less organized activities. There were tests of skill, some rather dangerous, like an Indian game (and mostly Indians participated) where men stood about twenty yards apart and took turns throwing spears at each other. The idea was to dodge the spear without moving your feet. If you moved your feet, you lost.

Tests of strength would come at the end of the Rendezvous, when the men would see how many 90-pound bales they could carry for a

measured mile up the portage towards Pigeon River. Pierre heard that
the record was 820 pounds! When he thought of how hard he had to
struggle to carry one 90-pound bale, he seriously wondered if he would
ever be strong enough to carry a second bale, let alone eight or nine.
When the day for the contest finally came, the winner was nearly 100
pounds short of the record, but it was still no small achievement. The
winner's name was Claude, and he was just about as broad as he was
tall.

Since the men were paid a part of their salary here, a good deal of
gambling took place. Much money was won and lost on an Indian
game called "Beg-ga-shah," in which several pieces of metal or other objects, colored on one side, were placed in a kettle and tossed in the air.
Bets were placed on the color combinations that would turn up. In
another game, the participants would bet on which of four moccasins
had a bullet or other object hidden in it. It amazed Pierre how many different ways the men could find to gamble away their hard-earned
wages.

Jean Baptiste had arranged to have most of his (and Pierre's) salary
deposited in Montreal for safe keeping and for Emile to use as needed.
But Pierre had five whole dollars he planned to blow at the Rendez-

The Great Hall at Grand Portage.

vous. The first dollar went for an Ostrich plume and the second for a voyageur's pipe. Jean Baptiste saw the latter transaction take place, but did not stop his nephew even though he felt he was too young to smoke. Instead, he offered to have a smoke with the boy, but first excused himself to get some special tobacco for the occasion. Pierre never knew what his uncle added. Jean Baptiste just told him that it was special and came from Brazil (as indeed it did), but he knew he had never been so sick in his life! He held out as long as he could, but finally excused himself and snuck off into the bushes to rid himself of more than he thought he could possibly have eaten on the whole trip.

Pierre never smoked again.

The next day wrestling matches were going on in an open, level area behind the stockade. Pierre was not surprised to find his uncle there, and as he approached him he heard a husky voyageur he did not know yell good naturedly, "Jean—Jean Baptiste—this year I beat you!"

As they met, the two shook hands and messed up each other's hair more like old friends, which they were, than rivals. But with the greeting out of the way, they stripped off their shirts and began circling each other like a couple of fighting cocks. After a few moves and feints, they came together like a couple of bull moose. Each tried to lift the other off the ground, but to no avail. Jean Baptiste suddenly dropped to his knees, wrapped his arms around his opponent's legs, raised up, and then leaned into the man when his feet cleared the ground. As the man's back hit the grass, Jean Baptiste was on top of him, trapping one of his opponent's arms against his head and putting his full weight on the man's chest. As the man on the bottom tried to roll and pitch him off or over, Jean Baptiste dug his toes into the soft earth and swung his body perpendicular—then he raised up on his toes and arched his back, putting more pressure on the man's chest. There were no referees and very few rules for these wrestling matches, but pinning an opponent's shoulders was not enough to secure a victory; you had to make him give up. So Jean Baptiste lifted up under the man's neck with his forearm without letting go of his hold, and then buried the front of his shoulder into the man's face so that he could not breathe. It wasn't long before Pierre heard a very muffled, "'Nough—enough!" And it was all over.

As Jean Baptiste helped the man, whose name Pierre never did learn, to his feet, they embraced and then the victim left with a wave and a cheerful shout, "Next year, Jean Baptiste, I get you next year!"

Pierre would have loved to have joined in the wrestling, but he looked in vain for someone near his age or even his build. He knew better than to bite off more than he could chew. Pierre had grown taller and more muscular, as tall as most of the crew. But his 150 pounds was no match for the mature, broad-shouldered voyageurs with their huge biceps and forearms.

With darkness came big campfires and dancing. There weren't many musical instruments available, just a fiddle or two, a few harmonicas, and a lot of beating time on anything noisy and handy. Of course, there were no women, but that didn't stop the men from dancing their jigs or locking arms over shoulders and joining in a big circle, going around and around the fire until someone dropped.

On such occasions, a traditional dance was performed by an older voyageur and a younger voyageur, and during a break in the action, Jean Baptiste suggested, "Pierre, let us do our dance—you know the one I mean—the one I taught you that always made Emile laugh."

Pierre's response was, "Oh, no—I'm not good enough—my voice still cracks when I sing."

But he knew there was no way out as the other voyageurs pushed him forward. Two packs were set on the ground about ten feet apart. Jean Baptiste and Pierre each sat on one at the outset, facing each other, with a kettle and wooden spoon in either hand. As each sang his solo part, he strutted and danced around his pack, singing and beating time on the kettle. When it came time for the chorus, the others formed a large circle around the soloists and danced, arms on shoulders, as they sang.

Pierre began:	"We are voyageurs starting on our way. Don't you see the people of the city watching us from the walls?" (In French, these lines all rhymed)
Jean Baptiste:	"Carry patience in your purse. You will need it when you get thirsty from continuous paddling and portaging. You will seldom rest."
Chorus:	"Dance pretty shepherdess, dance lightly!"
Pierre:	"Goodbye, Father, goodbye, Mother, goodbye Brother, too. Don't be sad, you will soon see your Pierre again."
Jean Baptiste:	"Go in your canoe and take your packs. You are about to leave your home and your relatives to go

up streams and across lakes, always harnessed to your pack and your canoe."

Pierre: "We are voyageurs and good fellows. We seldom eat but we often drink!"

Jean Baptiste: "If the mosquitoes sting your face and deafen your ears with their buzzing, endure them patiently, because they will show you how Satan will torture you in order to possess your pitiful soul!"

And on, and on, and on.

As the evening continued, there was considerable drinking. Voyageurs were usually allowed to imbibe only on special occasions, but this surely was one of them. Unfortunately for some, things got a little out of hand and good fun sometimes turned into fighting. But in the morning, all was forgotten except the headaches.

Pierre joined in the festivities wherever he could. He really enjoyed the Rendezvous, but for the first time he longed for someone his own age.

CHAPTER V
BOUNDARY WATERS

The combination of the squawking sea gulls, a light chill under a thin blanket, and the rising sun over Lake Superior made it difficult for even a teenager to sleep in, and when a phoebe perched on a bush directly over Pierre's head and began chirping in his ear, that was too much. Pierre got up.

It was the last day at Grand Portage. The Rendezvous was about over and most of the trade goods had already been portaged to Fort Charlotte on the Pigeon River. Jean Baptiste would be responsible for a flotilla of an even dozen canoes bound for Rainy Lake and Lake of the Woods, so he had to "check-out" with the traders in the Great House. He took Pierre with him, and our youngest voyageur was privileged to meet some of the heroic (and historic) figures of the great fur trade industry. It was the custom of as many of the partners of the North West Company as could to meet at Grand Portage during the Rendezvous. Because the British had taken over Canada in 1763 as a result of their defeat of the French, mostly in other parts of the world, the officers of the North West Company were all Scottish or English. Some of the really big names were gathered at Grand Portage that summer of 1797:

- Sir Alexander Mackenzie—the famous explorer who discovered a route to the Arctic by means of a river which still bears his name (in 1789). Just a few years later, in 1793, he had been the first to cross the northern part of the continent—all the way to the Pacific Ocean. The mystery of just how big North America really was had finally been solved.

- David Thompson—who had recently left the Hudson's Bay Company and had earned his fame as a surveyor and map maker.*

*Maps drawn with the assistance of modern day satellites reveal the amazing accuracy of Thompson's work.

- Simon Fraser—who at that time was in charge of
  the great North West post at Grand Portage.

As Pierre shook the hand of each man—while his proud uncle beamed—he was surprised to be greeted in French. Later, Jean Baptiste would explain that French was the official language of the fur trade and even the officers of the Hudson's Bay Company knew it well.

The Great House was teeming with people and activity. Pierre estimated there must have been a hundred men—each busy with his appropriate work. The fur industry had quite a caste system. Under the partners were the "bourgeois" or traders. Then came the "commis," who were clerks in training to become traders. Pierre was to learn later that these clerks supervised those voyageurs, out in the wintering posts, who were eligible to trade with the Indians—and he would have more than his share of trouble with one of them. Interpreters and guides were one level above the ordinary voyageurs who paddled and carried goods across the portages. The French called these hired men "engagés." All of them were licensed by the Canadian government.

David Thompson announced that this being Sunday morning, he would be leading a short church service. The voyageurs were a religious lot and many gathered around as the Englishman read three chapters from the Old Testament and a like number from the New, and then, after prayer, led the men in a hymn—all in French.

Later, Pierre observed to his uncle, "That church service was kind of different, no mass, no Communion wine, no Latin..."

"Well," Jean Baptiste replied, "Thompson is a Protestant, and they do things a little different, but I don't think the good Lord minds."

Pierre had heard about Protestants, but he had never met one until now.

Later that morning, the uncle and nephew resumed the drudgery of packing the 90-pound bales over the 8-1/2 mile portage, mostly uphill. Jean Baptiste carried three bales, as promised, so that Pierre would have to carry only one. That single bale was more than enough for any normal 15-year-old, but Pierre had trained his body well and he was far more muscular than most boys his age. Besides, Jean Baptiste had shown him how to balance the load perfectly on the strongest part of his back with the help of a tumpline or collar. He actually ran at a "dog-trot," leaning forward into the load. He was as grateful as anyone, however, when the crew made a stop ("posé") about every one-third mile to have a smoke. It was a hot, still July day, and the smoke hung like fog along the wooded path.

More than once, Pierre thanked his uncle for carrying the third bale. Normally voyageurs were paid an extra dollar for each bale over two on the longer portages, but, as we know, Jean Baptiste had bargained away that extra pay when he asked to bring his nephew along.

As the sun set that night, even the combination of aching muscles and the pesty mosquitoes could not keep Pierre awake. He just nestled down in some long grass by the river, pulled his blanket over his head, and went to sleep.

Sir Alexander Mackenzie was also headed West and he and his entourage had arrived on the river bank just before dark. In the morning, his canoe was the first one in the water. Pierre was awed by Mackenzie's special crew. First of all, the canoe was a little longer than the 25-foot north canoe the others were using, and it was beautifully decorated with blue and orange trim. According to Jean Baptiste, the men were among the strongest and best paddlers of all voyageurs. They were dressed in their finest, and as they pushed out from shore, one of the men towards the stern carefully rose to his feet. He was dressed in kilts and full Scottish regalia. Gracefully he picked up his bagpipes and began to play! The men dug their paddles in time to the spirited music, and the canoe shot forward at a speed Pierre did not know was possible. Sir Alexander sat in the middle, leaning majestically against a backrest, a high silk hat perched with dignity on his head.

"Now that's traveling in style!" Pierre observed.

Soon their own canoes were loaded and the flotilla of 12, which Jean Baptiste commanded, was on its way. The canoes, of course, were a good deal smaller than those they had been using on the Great Lakes and carried a crew of only eight. Jean Baptiste chose to ride in the prow this time because there were so many more rapids and underwater hazards, like reefs, rocks, and sand bars. The steersman was a jovial little fellow named Jacque La Vallee. He was always teasing Pierre and didn't seem to mind the boy's endless questions.

Pierre studied the others. His seatmate, Jean-Paul, who seemed the oldest of the crew, was also the quietest. Directly in front of him were Joseph and Antoine, who had been partners so long they argued and fought like brothers. Then, in front of the bales of trade goods were two of the ugliest men he had ever seen. He never did know their real names, only their nicknames, which were the opposite of what the men really looked like. Pierre soon learned this was characteristic of the voyageurs' sense of humor. The one had a nostril missing—he said it was bitten off in a fight—and a badly scarred right cheek which he claimed was a souvenir from a battle with a bear. The men called him "Angel." The second man had a head too big for his body, a lantern jaw, huge teeth spaced far apart, no hair, and arms that were too long. The other voyageurs called him, "Little Maiden"!

Jean Baptiste's canoe led the way, and he served as his own guide, he had been to Rainy Lake and Lake of the Woods so many times.

"It was good being first in line," Pierre thought. "This way I get a better chance to see animals and birds and I have a clear view of the scenery."

Pierre especially enjoyed the lakes. The rivers were actually more beautiful, but so scary! He was sure that they would perish in every rapids, but Jean Baptiste's expert skill and strength, from his position in the prow of the boat, brought the canoe through unscathed every time. Then too the rivers had some rapids the North West Company forbade the voyageurs to navigate. They had cost the lives of so many men and the loss of so much goods. These, plus the cascades and waterfalls, meant difficult portages, and there were lots of them. Most were both muddy and rocky and sometimes slippery. It was very easy to lose one's balance, and Pierre did several times. In most cases he was able to crash into some bushes which broke his fall, but on two occasions he went face first into the trail and was lucky to escape with bruised and scraped knees. And when you are face down in mud with 90 pounds on your back, it isn't easy to get up!

Because their flotilla was going only as far as Lake of the Woods, there was no big hurry, so the men made camp well before dark each day and did not start the next morning until after sun-up. The steady pace ate up the miles, however, as the fleet of canoes traveled up the Pigeon River and encountered the Partridge, Big Rock, and Caribou Portages. Then came Fowl Lakes, the Moose Portage, and Moose Lake, where they camped the second night. Then came Big Cherry, Vascoux, and Little Cherry Portages and an overnight camp on spectacular Mountain Lake. A heavy haze of smoke hung over the water from a forest fire somewhere in the northwest.

Although the travel was seldom easy, after leaving Pigeon River they at least paddled with the current, having crossed a continental divide.

Next camp Watape Portage, Rove Lake, Long Portage, Rose Lake, Marten Portage, Perch Portage, and Height of Land. Here the voyageurs made camp early because Jean Baptiste had promised the men time off for a special meal and a little celebrating. While some men helped the cook make camp, others scattered into the woods in search

The tumpline across his forehead gave Pierre balance as he leaned forward into the load and took off at a trot.

of fresh meat for a mulligan stew. Shots were soon heard here and there back in the forest, and the hunters brought back a real mixed bag of partridge, passenger pigeons, squirrels, rabbits, and ducks. That night, as the men enjoyed the after-dinner campfire and their wine, the first since Grand Portage, the man the others called "Angel" spoke up: "Jean, Jean Baptiste, it occurs to me that we have among us a pork eater who needs converting into a Nor'wester!"

The men's eyes sought out Pierre and then supported Angel's comment with such remarks as:

"You bet your buttons!"

"That's for sure."

"Let's have an initiation!"

Pierre squirmed.

"But not tonight." Angel went on. "This calls for proper planning and a celebration all its own. I suggest Rebecca Falls as the place, or the nearest camp site to the falls."

And then he added, very slowly and in a deep voice, "That will give our young voyageur...time...to contemplate.....his.....fate!"

Pierre's questions about the initiation ceremony in the past had gone unanswered, and he was more than a little worried. He had no idea what lay ahead, but this he knew; he was determined to take it like a man.

Much water lay ahead before they would reach Rebecca Falls, and many portages as well. After North Lake came Staircase Portage (well named) and then beautiful Gunflint Lake. After Wooden Horse Portage and Pine Portage came Lake Saganaga with its many islands. Rough water convinced Jean Baptiste to make early camp on a large island with a sheltering cove. There was no threat of rain and the canoes were left loaded, moored to shore by cedar poles which lay across the gunnels of each and which were then anchored to the shoreline.

After Swamp Portage came Cyprus Lake, named improperly for the cedars which lined its shores. Then came Little Knife Portage, Knife Lake, and Big Knife Portage. Carp Lake was next, also misnamed. The Europeans had mistakenly called suckers "carp." Then came Prairie Portage. Here an old man named Bouché baked and sold bread.

Pierre couldn't believe it. He just shook his head and muttered, "A bakery in the wilderness?"

The old baker, as soon as he had sold his bread, engaged Pierre in conversation. When the boy asked Bouché if he had ever been a voyageur, he responded, "I could carry, paddle, walk, and sing with any man I ever knew! I was 41 years in service to one company or another, 24 years a canoe man. No portage was ever too long for me. Fifty songs could I sing. I saved the lives of 10 voyageurs. I've had 12 wives and 6 running dogs. I spent all my money in pleasure, until now. Oh, that I could be young again like you, my son. I would spend my whole life the same way over. There's no life so happy as a voyageur's life!" The old man's testimony left no doubt in Pierre's mind he had chosen the right occupation.

Soon they were off again, with Whitewood Lake and River (now called Basswood) coming next. The river was often narrow and had a whole series of rapids and cascades. Then came Horse Portage (actually two portages), Wheelbarrow Portage, and Lower Falls. Croche (Crooked) Lake was next. Jean Baptiste directed the canoes to a flat granite wall decorated with Indian artwork. He then pointed out a high crevasse where the wooden weathered shafts of arrows were barely visible. Jean Baptiste explained, "The arrows were shot there by a Prairie Sioux raiding party as a testimony of their marksmanship to all who pass this way."

This triggered a flow of questions from Pierre:

"Are the Sioux still around?"

"When was the last time a voyageur was attacked by Indians?"

"Do most Indians like voyageurs?"

The correct answers to these questions would have quieted Pierre's fears. But the men chose, instead, to manufacture all sorts of wild stories.

After Crooked Lake, only a single portage stood between Pierre and his initiation at Rebecca Falls. When Angel pointed this out to Pierre, the young man suddenly became uncharacteristically quiet. Ever since it had been decided to have an initiation, Pierre had been transformed into the most helpful, hard-working, well-behaved youngster imaginable. He was like a boy just before Christmas. He almost never rested his paddle; he did more than his share on portages and around camp and kept asking, "Is there anything I can do to help?"

He hoped everyone would notice and be easier on him during the initiation.

The voyageurs made camp early and several again took to the woods in search of game for supper. Pierre borrowed his uncle's muzzle loader and slipped off with the steersman, Jacque La Vallee. Normally, Pierre would have enjoyed hunting, but his mind was on the initiation planned for that evening and he neither concentrated on seeing game or hitting the target. Pierre missed all three chances—two pigeons and a part-ridge. The fact that Jacque connected on four plump birds, three of them missed by Pierre, didn't help matters. And the steersman enjoyed rubbing it in. Finally, when almost back to camp, a spruce hen fluttered up into a white pine and just sat there.

"All right, Pierre," Jacque chuckled, "Let's see if you can hit a sitting target!"

Pierre did, and felt better.

It was a warm evening, and the voyageurs built a campfire for light (rather than for heat) and, after finishing their meal, sat down one by one in a huge circle.

Pierre grew uneasy as he noticed whispered conversations and overheard occasional phrases like:

"But he's only a boy."
"Isn't that a bit rough?"
"That would be *too* mean!"

Actually, the ceremony was terribly simple and anything but rough. The fun was in making the pork eater worry.

At long last, about the time Pierre was ready to "head for the hills," Angel got slowly to his feet and looked around the circle as though try-ing to spot his victim. Then, allowing his eyes to focus on Pierre who was sitting back in the shadows as though he hoped no one would notice him and the whole thing would be forgotten, Angel spoke—very slowly, "Well...I suppose we'd better get on with it.

Pierre, Pierre La Vérendrye! Present yourself!"

Hesitantly, the boy arose and stumbled over his own feet as he slouched to within ten yards of Angel. Then he stopped, his eyes look-ing down at the ground.

"Pierre!" Angel commanded, "Present yourself here!" He pointed to a spot immediately in front of him.

The boy obeyed.

Angel placed his big hand on the back of Pierre's neck and slowly turned him around to face the fire. He then addressed his comrades, "Fellow voyageurs, I bring to your attention this insignificant, unworthy pork eater. He has had the audacity to travel with us Nor'westers all this way without a proper initiation. I say the time has come to bring him into the fold properly or send him back to Montreal with the first canoe we meet. Do you agree mates?"

A loud chorus of "yeahs" and "ayes" echoed into the night.

"All right, then, we shall proceed!"

Angel swung the boy around again so that they stood facing each other, eyeball to eyeball, except that Pierre kept snatching glances at the ground.

"Look at me, boy!" Angel thundered.

Pierre obeyed unflinchingly, his body stiff as a board.

"Now, you pork-eating scum," Angel snarled, "If you consider yourself worthy to become a Nor'wester, you must take two oaths before these voyageurs and your God. If you agree to each of them, answer by saying, 'I do so solemnly swear.'"

Pierre remained silent.

"Do you hear me, boy?" Angel again bellowed.

"Oui, monsieur." Pierre replied in a whisper.

"Are you willing to take the oaths no matter what they are?" Angel asked.

"I guess so," came the weak reply.

"Yes or no?" Angel demanded.

"Y-y-y-yes," Pierre stuttered.

"Then we shall proceed. Remember to answer by saying, 'I do so solemnly swear.'" Angel paused for effect and then asked, "Do you swear that you will never mess with another voyageur's woman?"

"I do so solemnly swear," Pierre said loudly and with determination.

"And do you swear never to let a pork eater make this journey without an initiation ceremony such as this?"

"I do so solemnly swear." Pierre responded with assurance.

"Bring forth the cedar bough!" Angel ordered.

The man they called "Little Maiden" came out of the shadows with a cedar branch in one hand and a kettle of the foulest smelling, slimiest swamp water he could find in the other.

Majestically, Angel took the cedar bough from his partner, dipped it slowly into the pot, and sprinkled Pierre again and again with the awful, smelly, scummy water. He then triumphantly proclaimed, "I now pronounce you—a Nor'wester!"

Cheers rang from the nearly 100 voyageurs and a dozen men rose to their feet and fired as many well-spaced shots into the black sky.

Angel took one step forward and kissed Pierre on both cheeks. Pierre smiled broadly and asked, "Is that all there is to it?"

"Not quite!" Angel replied, "You *stink*!"

And with that signal, many hands grabbed Pierre's arms and legs, lifting him high in the air as the throng moved to the water's edge, and threw him—kicking and screaming—into the murky depths!

A few minutes later as Pierre was hanging his wet clothing by the fire, Angel said, "One thing more. If you will get up at daybreak and climb that big, red pine over there, and chop off all the limbs except the top dozen or so, we will name that pine and this point in your honor to remember this special occasion."

Pierre slept fitfully through the night and rolled out of his blanket just as the first light of dawn made objects distinguishable. The idea of having a point of land named for him was really exciting. He tucked a hatchet in his sash and shinnied up the big red pine Angel had pointed out the night before in less than a minute—stopping a dozen branches from the top. With quick slashes of the hatchet, he trimmed the tree naked of all other branches working his way down the trunk. In minutes it was all over—mission accomplished.

When Pierre hit the ground, he noticed that the cook was the only one up; no one else had moved. The sound of the blows of his hatchet and the falling branches had aroused no one. So he sauntered over to Louis—that was the cook's name—and made conversation as he watched him prepare breakfast.

"Well, Louis, I was up before you *this* morning." Pierre began.

"More or less," the cook responded.

"What do you mean, 'more or less'?" Pierre asked.

"Don't you know a cook is up off and on all night?" Louis returned.

"Really?" Pierre responded in genuine surprise.

"Sure," Louis added, "I have to keep the fires going so the pots will simmer all night."

"What's your recipe?" Pierre asked—half out of curiosity and half just making conversation.

"Well," Louis began, "It isn't very complicated. I start by putting about 8 gallons of water in each kettle—I've made a scratch on the inside of each pot to show me how far to fill it. Then, I add 9 quarts of dried corn. For seasoning, I cut two pounds of salt pork into strips for each container and stir it in. By morning it's usually just the right thickness. Here's how I tell."

Louis picked up a stick and stood it on end on the bottom of the middle of the pot. The stick slowly fell to one side.

"Nope," the cook said, "Not quite thick enough. When the stick stands on end by itself and doesn't fall over, the brew is done."

Louis had spooned some dough on some flat rocks propped up by the fire. He knew by experience they would be done the same time as the porridge. When they were ready, Louis turned to Pierre and said, "If you want to help, break the biscuits into pieces and scatter them on top of the brew."

"Sure," Pierre replied, and tossed each biscuit from hand to hand to cool it off before carrying out his assignment.

Voyageurs seem to have a way of sensing when food is ready, and the men began rolling out and gathering around the kettles with their wooden spoons—enjoying a visit while they ate.

Pierre watched for Angel and as soon as he was up, ran to his side asking, "Did you see I trimmed the pine tree like you said?"

"See ya? I *heard* ya!" Angel grumbled—but then smiled, showing his widely spaced teeth. Putting one hand on Pierre's shoulder, he turned him facing the tree, and then solemnly proclaimed, "I pronounce this place to be—*Pierre's Point!*"

Before the sun was very far above the trees, the men were once again in their canoes heading west. After Pewarbic (now called Bottle Portage) came Lac La Croix. It was a windy day, and Jean Baptiste made good use of several of the lake's 260 islands to shelter the canoes from the choppy waves.

Jacque, the steersman, told Pierre, "There's a route northeast from this lake that ends up on the Kaministiquia River and hits Lake Superior north of Grand Portage on Thunder Bay—you probably stopped at the trading post at the mouth of the river on your way to the Rendezvous. It is the old route."

Pierre said that he remembered.

"It takes a little longer than our route," he went on, "So not many use it any more. And by the way, this lake, La Croix, is named for a man who drowned here. He was with De Noyon, the explorer who discovered Lake of the Woods."

As they made camp that night, Jean Baptiste remarked to the men, "This makes 10 days since we left Fort Charlotte—not bad time for not hurrying."

Next morning they covered the portage to Loon Lake and Loon River. On Little Vermillion Lake they passed an old, abandoned trading house. That night, Jean Baptiste told Pierre that the post had been there "for as long as anyone could remember," and added, "Some say it was started by Bourassa, a man who was in your great-grandfather's command."

Then came Portage Lake. Namakan River was avoided on orders from the North West Company because of its many rapids. Namakan Lake (then called "Mekan") followed. Next was Kettle Falls—and at long last—Rainy Lake.

Once on Rainy (the French called it Lac La Pluie) the voyageurs picked up the tempo of their chanties and dug their paddles a little deeper and more briskly. The post at the end of the lake was the final destination for half the canoes, and for the other six it meant a few days of rest for the occupants before going on to the Lake of the Woods.

As the old fort came into view, it was one of the more memorable sites of the journey for young Pierre. The clearing was bustling with activity; a large Indian village literally surrounded the fort; scores of canoes were pulled up on the bench; and people were everywhere. Barking dogs added to the excitement as they greeted each arrival.

As their own canoe pulled into the shallows, Jacque and Jean Baptiste jumped into the waist-deep water and steadied the vessel while the other men unloaded the trade goods. Once empty, the canoe was beached—well out of the way of any unexpected storms. Pierre was now free to explore. His heart beat just a little faster with excitement as he surveyed all the activity, and he said to himself, "I'm finally starting to feel like a real voyageur!"

CHAPTER VI

ON TO THE
LAKE OF THE WOODS

The brief stay at the Rainy Lake Post was relatively uneventful. It would have been totally pleasant, had it not been for the presence of a young man about Pierre's age—one Jonathan Briggs, Junior. Jonathan was best described by Angel, who called him "an arrogant, young bully." He was the son of Jonathan Briggs, Senior, who was classified as a "commis" (a clerk in training to become a trader) and who was scheduled to operate the Lake of the Woods post where Jean Baptiste and Pierre would be working all winter. The junior Briggs came by his arrogance quite naturally. He inherited it from his father. Angel had an additional word to characterize the father: "pompous." In fact, the chief trader at the Rainy Lake post, George Mc Kay, apologized to Jean Baptiste for placing him and his men under such a tyrant. He explained, "Briggs has relatives high up in the company and I've been ordered to put him in charge of the wintering post. As a matter of fact, this will be his second year."

Jean Baptiste was easy to get along with and he promised, "My men and I will do our best to satisfy him and will try to give him no cause to complain."

Mc Kay expressed his appreciation, but added, "I don't trust the man; there is something about him that rattles my kettle. I know you'll be working under him, Jean Baptiste, but keep an eye on him for me. I've had complaints from the Lake of the Woods Indians that he cheats them, giving them fewer trade goods than he should for their furs, but his books checked out. He had the right amount of furs for the trade goods he had in his inventory. He would have to be keeping furs for himself, but that doesn't make sense. There is no way he could get them back to Montreal. I don't know what to make of the stories."

Jean Baptiste agreed to keep his eyes open.

When the day came for the remaining six canoes to depart for Lake of the Woods, the voyageurs were, at first, engaged in reloading their vessels with trade goods and supplies for the winter. Pierre, doing his share, had a bale of kettles and pans on his shoulders as he came trotting around the corner of the supply house with his head down, full speed ahead, when he ran smack into Jonathan Briggs, Junior. Both boys were staggered by the collision and, as they bounced apart, both nearly fell down.

Briggs blurted out, "Watch where you're going!"

And Pierre muttered, "Sorry," not wanting to have trouble with his boss's son.

Then, as Pierre regained his balance and started forward, the Briggs boy stuck out his foot and sent the young voyageur sprawling, the pack going one way and Pierre the other.

"You did that on purpose!" Pierre shouted.

"So I did. But you asked for it!" Briggs replied and then added, "Wanna make something of it?"

Pierre hesitated. In the first place, he didn't want trouble with the son of his boss. And in the second place, as he looked up at his challenger, he realized how much bigger he was, not only taller, but broader and heavier. "Mostly fat," Pierre calculated in a split second. Then he began thinking how he could have been seriously injured and how unfair it was tripping someone with a load, and he suddenly heard himself saying, "Yeah, you bet I want to make something of it!"

It was then that Pierre learned an important lesson; never accept a challenge to fight when you are lying on your back, propped up on your elbows. As he started to raise up, Jonathan Briggs landed on top of him, full force, with all of his 175 pounds, fat or no fat! Pierre found himself squashed on his back with a face full of stomach. At least his arms were free, and he quickly encircled the bigger boy's ample middle with a bear hug and tried to roll him over or off, but he couldn't budge him. He tried bridging his body up but was barely able to raise himself and his heavy load an inch or two off the ground. Briggs had dug his toes into the ground, arched his back so that his full weight was on Pierre's chest and head, and had encircled the base of a handy small tree with his arms. Pierre bucked and squirmed and bucked and squirmed some more, but to no avail. After what seemed like forever, young Briggs asked triumphantly, "Had enough?"

Pierre couldn't have answered if he had wanted to, his adversary's big, soft belly had engulfed his face and he could hardly breathe.

Briggs had dug his toes into the ground, arched his back so that his full weight was on Pierre's chest and head, and had encircled the base of a handy small tree with his arms.

"That's all right," Briggs sneered, "I've got plenty of time." And he pushed down all the harder.

Pierre finally tried to think, what had Jean Baptiste taught him? Was Briggs vulnerable in any way?

He realized one thing, Briggs should have made himself perpendicular to his body for better control. Of course, Pierre had no way of knowing the reason he couldn't roll him off was because he was holding onto a tree. He had concluded he was just too big and stronger than he had looked. So he did the next best thing. He resumed wriggling and squirming. But this time he pushed up and forward on his opponent's flabby sides. Slowly but surely, Pierre slid out between Brigg's big, fat legs. The larger boy realized he was losing control of Pierre and finally had to let go of the tree, but before he could get a new hold, Pierre had escaped and was on his feet. As Briggs clumsily tried to get to his, Pierre drove his shoulder into his opponent's right side with all of his strength. The fat boy wheezed as the air went out of him and he collapsed to the ground. In a flash, Pierre pried him over on his back. Now all of Briggs' weight became a handicap as it made it harder for him to maneuver or raise up, and Pierre's strong arms soon locked Jonathan's right arm against his face as he (Pierre) sprawled out at right angles to his opponent. By raising up on his toes he pushed all his 150 pounds down on Briggs' chest and was in complete control. The bigger boy kicked and squirmed but to no avail; Pierre just tightened his hold, while his opponent only wore himself out.

"All right, big boy," Pierre said through clenched teeth, "Have **you** had enough?"

Pierre didn't have to ask twice. Jonathan Briggs knew he'd had it and hissed, "You win this time, but next time you won't get away from me."

As Pierre let him up, he suddenly realized the fight had drawn quite a crowd, including a very interested father and uncle. As soon as Jonathan saw his father he alibied, "He started it!" pointing to Pierre.

But who should appear at this point but George Mc Kay, who said, "I saw the whole thing from my window, and I'd say your boy asked for it, Jonathan. He tripped young La Vefendrye with a pack on his back."

The younger Briggs knew better than to argue with the commandant and just hung his head.

Jean Baptiste broke the silence, "Boys will be boys. As long as no one was hurt, let's shake hands and forget it."

With that, he pushed Pierre forward. Pierre slowly put his hand out.

Young Briggs finally took it briefly but looked the other way and quickly walked off.

Later that day, as the small convoy was about to start out for Lake of the Woods, Jean Baptiste suggested to Jonathan Briggs, Senior, "Why not let your son ride in our canoe with Pierre; it will help them make up and become friends."

The elder Briggs quickly agreed.

It was the custom of the voyageurs to give passengers a "piggy-back" ride to the canoe so they need not get their boots and clothing wet, and Jean Baptiste quickly invited young Briggs to hop on his back and ride in his canoe. Jean Baptiste purposely planted him on a bale in front of Pierre so the boys could not ignore each other. But ignore each other they did. Not a word passed between them the whole day. Come evening, Jean Baptiste selected a sand bar to make camp, and as he and the steersman jumped into the water to steady the canoe, young Briggs finally broke the silence. "Pierre," he began, "Let's see if you're man enough to carry me to shore."

"I think I can handle that," the young voyageur replied, and hopped overboard, allowing the heavier boy to climb onto his back.

The beach was only about 30 feet away and Pierre, who was accustomed to carrying the awkward bales, had little trouble with his human cargo. Briggs had been sure Pierre could not do it and would probably stumble and fall and be embarrassed. So as they reached dry ground, he couldn't resist kicking one heel into Pierre's stomach. That did it! Pierre grunted, then quickly turned back into the river, and once the water was waist deep, dumped Briggs. Totally immersed and looking like a drowned rat, the big boy floundered to his feet and came at Pierre swinging. Being more agile, Pierre sidestepped the charge and got behind the other boy as he went past. He then attacked from the rear, adding to Briggs' momentum, and drove him up onto the shore, where he finally stumbled and went face-first into the sand, Pierre on top. The bigger boy got to his knees with his rider hanging on. Pierre jumped off and allowed his opponent to start to get to his feet. When Briggs was still off balance, he tackled him from the side, again driving him to the ground, the momentum carrying him over onto his back. Pierre was in control. He caught Jonathan in a headlock and his well-muscled arm squeezed the big boy's neck like a vice.

"That's about enough." Pierre heard Jean Baptiste's familiar voice say. And he felt his uncle's huge hands grab him by his shirt collar and his waist band and lift him off.

Pierre was afraid his uncle didn't know how the fight started and why he had dumped the younger Briggs in the river, so he began to explain, "He kicked me in the stomach when he was on my back."

"I don't care who started it. You boys are going to have to learn to get along." Jean Baptiste replied sternly.

The two Briggs just walked away, but Pierre enjoyed those snatches of conversation between father and son he was able to pick up.

"You should have handled him; you're a lot bigger. You've lost twice."

"I know I'm bigger, but you wouldn't believe the muscles he's got from paddling and carrying bundles. Besides, he doesn't fight fair."

"Well, it's obvious you can't handle him so leave him alone, just don't start anything."

"Ya, you always stick up for the other guy. It's always *my* fault. You always assume *I* start the trouble."

Pierre especially enjoyed the way in which young Briggs had to "punctuate" every sentence by spitting out the gravel he got in his mouth as he landed face-first on the beach.

Pierre looked at his uncle, and they exchanged winks.

CHAPTER VII
JEAN BAPTISTE'S
SURPRISE

Two days after leaving the sand bar camp on the Rainy River—after winding their way among scores of heavily timbered islands which gave the Lake of the Woods its name—the convoy of canoes arrived at its destination, Turtle Lake Portage. Pierre, paddling in the lead canoe, had his first glimpse of the trading post, which would be his home for the winter, as they passed through the narrow, rock-faced channel that joins huge Sabaskong Bay of Lake of the Woods with tiny Turtle Lake. On the opposite shore stood a small stockade of sorts that really wouldn't keep anybody out who wanted to get in. Pierre was able to make out several small log cabins and a few traditional bark and hide-covered Indian lodges scattered on either side of the enclosure. Although the post was a far cry from the impressive operation at Grand Portage, or even on Rainy Lake, Pierre really wasn't disappointed or surprised at what he saw. Jean Baptiste had described the place in response to his endless questions as, "a small wintering post on a narrow isthmus of land between a small lake and Whitefish Bay."

He had also explained, "No traders are there in the summer. In fact, the post is quite temporary; it is a kind of an experiment to see if a trader's presence will encourage the Indians of that area to hunt and trap more, in that way increasing the fur trade."

Jean Baptiste further described the location as "strategic" in that it could easily serve most Indian villages on the lake, including a fairly large settlement located a couple of miles east, on the north shore of Sabaskong Bay. He had also explained that the company was more than a little concerned with the interest of the rival Hudson's Bay Company in the Lake of the Woods area. He had pointed out, enroute, recently abandoned Hudson's Bay posts on the Rainy River just below Manitou Falls and at the river's mouth. In regard to the latter, Jean Baptiste had said, "I'm surprised the post is closed. Mc Kay said that it was still in use last winter."

Mc Kay had also told Jean Baptiste, "Rumor has it that the Hudson's Bay Company has withdrawn its operations to the northern part of Lake of the Woods because they found they could not compete with us on Rainy River. If this is true, it makes the Turtle Portage operation all the more important to the North West Company."

The sprint across the small lake took only minutes and a couple of dozen Indians quickly gathered on the shore to welcome the white men, most of whom they knew from previous years.

Pierre joined the other voyageurs in unloading the canoes and carrying the parcels into the storehouse inside the stockade. Young Briggs had avoided Pierre ever since their second fight—just as his father had advised—and Pierre was careful to avoid further possibilities of a confrontation by not handling any goods marked for the trader's cabin, which was also within the stockade. He was surprised to see his uncle walk off with some of the Indians before the unloading had been completed, but thought little of it. When he finished his work and the canoes had been pulled up on the beach, he looked around for Jean Baptiste, but he was nowhere in sight. Pierre noticed, however, that both their duffle bags were still down by the water's edge, so he planted himself on his own bag and waited. In a few minutes, an Indian lad he judged to be about his own age, approached his uncle's duffle, stared momentarily at Pierre, pointed at the bag and said in French, "I take!"

Pierre couldn't believe what he had heard, but quickly responded as he got to his feet, "Oh no you don't!"

The young Indian hesitated a moment, and then again said, "I take," picked up the bag and walked away.

Pierre was stunned. But after the boy had taken a dozen or so steps, he came to his wits and decided he had to act. So he ran after him and made a flying tackle! The Indian, of course, let go of the bag and the two boys were soon locked in combat, rolling down the incline toward the lake. The Indian was a little taller than Pierre, but more slender, and for a few minutes it was a good match, with first one boy having the advantage and then the other. But Pierre's greater strength and knowledge of wrestling prevailed and he ended up lying perpendicular to his opponent with the Indian boy's arm trapped against his own face.

"If I let you go will you leave the bag alone?" Pierre asked.

No answer.

"Unless you promise, I won't let you up."

Still no answer.

The Indian youth had stopped his struggling and could breath only when Pierre let him. So he felt in complete control and confident he had made his point, even though the boy would not answer. The thought that the Indian might not fully understand crossed his mind. Besides, having young Briggs for an enemy was enough. He had hoped to find someone his age for a friend and he surely didn't want all of the Indians mad at him. So—carefully and cautiously, Pierre stood up with one final warning, "If you touch the bag, I'll fight you again!"

The young Indian scrambled to his feet and just stared at Pierre—still breathing hard. Then without warning, quick as a fox the Indian's foot lashed out—kicking Pierre in the groin! Pierre doubled up in pain as the Indian picked up the bag and trotted off around the corner of the nearest cabin.

It was several minutes before Pierre had recovered enough to limp after him, angry with himself for not being on guard and furious with the Indian boy for his treacherous attack. There were a half-dozen cabins and lodges which the boy could have entered, so Pierre just stood there—bewildered.

At that moment, Jean Baptiste poked his head out of the nearest cabin door and said, "Ah, there you are. Come on in, I have someone I want you to meet."

Pierre was hurt and confused, but he was glad he had found his uncle and meekly obeyed.

"If I let you up will you leave the bag alone?" Pierre asked.

The small cabin seemed full of people. An Indian man and woman stood next to Jean Baptiste. Two little children, a boy and a girl, were playing on the floor. His eye caught his uncle's duffle bag—sitting in the middle of the room! And then he saw him—the Indian boy he had just fought—standing like a statue with his back against the far wall and looking very much upset by Pierre's entrance.

Pierre blurted out, "You!"

The Indian youth blurted back, "You!"

Jean Baptiste looked first at Pierre and then at the young Indian and said, "It seems I'm too late. It appears you two have already met."

Pierre replied, still shouting, "He stole your duffle bag!"

The Indian boy replied just as loudly, in quite good French, "I not steal it. I get it for Jean Baptiste. He send me."

"That's true." Jean Baptiste assured Pierre as he walked towards him, took him gently by the arm, and led him across the room to where the Indian boy was backed against the wall. He then put his hand behind the Indian lad's neck and pulled him away from the wall, close to Pierre, and said, quietly and calmly, "Pierre, Solomon, I want you each to meet," Jean Baptiste paused for effect and then went on, "I want you each to meet—your brother."

The full impact of what Jean Baptiste had said took minutes to sink in. The first sound to break the silence was the soft crying of the Indian woman—although she had known all along. The Indian youth was first to speak, "What you say?" he asked in bewilderment.

Pierre found his own voice, "How can that be? How can an Indian be my brother?"

"Look at Solomon closely, Pierre. Just because he is wearing only a loin cloth and head band does not make him an Indian."

For the first time, Pierre saw that the black hair pushed behind the boy's head band was even curlier than his own, and even though he had the high cheekbones of an Indian, his skin was lighter than most, and his eyes, they were hauntingly like his father's!

"You see, Pierre, Solomon," Jean Baptiste went on, "Your father really had two families. Solomon is six months younger than you, Pierre. Your father's Indian wife was Winnetka, here. After your father died, she took Wa-ge-mah-wub as her husband, and these are their two children. Because your father had taken Winnetka as his second wife before your mother died, he felt—well—he felt guilty, and couldn't bring himself to tell you. But I know he had planned to bring you here so you could meet his other family when you were old enough. We talked of it often. Winnetka knew about your father's white wife and knew about you. But we all thought it best you and Solomon not know until you were old enough to understand. My brother—your father—spoke often of his hope that someday, when you both knew, you would forgive him."

When Jean Baptiste finished, there was complete silence. Finally, Winnetka spoke to Solomon in the Cree language, "Aren't you going to welcome your brother?"

Jean Baptiste looked at Pierre, and said, "Aren't you going to say something to your brother?"

Sheepishly, cautiously, Solomon extended his hand as his father had taught him. Pierre started to raise his, but suddenly overcome with emotion, threw both arms around the boy he had hated with a passion only minutes before, and whispered, "My brother—my brother—my brother!"

Solomon managed to stutter, "Y-y-yes—brother." And after some hesitation, returned the embrace in earnest.

As the boys separated, Winnetka came across the room and touched Pierre on the arm. She spoke little French, but managed to say, "Francois' son welcome. This Francois' cabin. You welcome stay here."

Jean Baptiste interrupted, "That is nice of you, Winnetka, but I would be lonesome in my cabin. I need Pierre with me. Maybe Solomon could live with us so that the brothers would get to know each other better. Please don't answer now. Talk it over with Wa-ge-mah-wub and Solomon. But whatever you decide, we will all be family."

That night, when Pierre and Jean Baptiste were settled in their own cabin, there was much conversation. Pierre's thoughts were filled with mixed emotions. He was disappointed in his father and really could not accept what he had done, even though his uncle told him he wasn't the only voyageur to have two families. On the other hand, he was grateful to his father for giving him what he had always wanted, a brother.

His original dislike for Solomon had quickly melted when he realized he had been sent by Jean Baptiste to fetch his bag. He even forgave him for the kick that hurt so much, when his uncle explained that Solomon had been taught that there were no rules to real fighting; only winning was important, because your life often depended on the outcome.

Pierre told his uncle, "You know, the name 'Solomon' rings a bell. Once in awhile my father would call me 'Solomon,' and when I would ask why, he would say that Solomon was his favorite character in the Bible and that I reminded him of Solomon because I was so wise."

Pierre couldn't decide whether he was happy or sad, but just before he drifted off to sleep, he asked his uncle, "Are you awake?"

Jean Baptiste assured him that he was.

"Well," Pierre continued, "I just wanted to say—*you* are my father now. Is that all right with you?"

The gruff Frenchman was touched and answered, "All right with me? Pierre, hearing you say that has just made me about the happiest man on Lake of the Woods—no—maybe the happiest man in all Canada!"

CHAPTER VIII
EXPLORING THE LAKE OF THE WOODS

The morning after Pierre's dramatic discovery that he had a brother, he awoke unsure whether it was all a dream or for real. Of course, as his head cleared, he knew he had, in fact, met his brother and couldn't wait to know him better—much better. Jean Baptiste, however, advised Pierre that would have to wait until later in the day. The first order of business was for the voyageurs to meet with Jonathan Briggs, Sr., to receive their orders for the next few weeks. Thus it was that Pierre's breakfast scarcely had a chance to settle before he found himself with the other voyageurs, listening to the pompous trader outline his priorities.

"To start with," Briggs began, "this stockade needs fixing—bad. I realize we are probably in no danger of attack by the Sioux, but it's hard to have the respect of the local Indians when the gate is hanging by one hinge and a dozen posts are missing. And the posts in that corner," Briggs went on as he pointed in back of his audience, "were pretty badly burned when somebody's campfire got too close. Anyway, I demand respect, and I cannot expect respect with the stockade looking like this!"

"Secondly," the trader continued, "My cabin leaks. In fact, the roof's about gone! I don't expect shingles out here in this God-forsaken country but I do expect to stay dry. So I'll appoint one crew to work on the stockade and another to cut fresh spruce boughs and thatch me a good roof. Later we'll replace it with bark."

"And then we'd better let the Indians on the lake know we are here and want their furs." Briggs went on. "And we've got to find out if any of the Hudson's Bay boys are still on the lake. We've got to know if we're going to have any competition—that will make a big difference in what we're going to have to give for furs."

"Any questions?" the commis asked.

There were none.

"All right then—here are your assignments."

Briggs took a piece of paper from his pocket and read off the different crews with a straw-boss for each.

Pierre was delighted when he heard his name among those who would visit the Indian villages and look for the competition, and he was both impressed and pleased when Briggs named Jean Baptiste as the man in charge. He was a little surprised that Briggs would bestow such an honor on his uncle; he thought the trader didn't like Jean Baptiste—especially since he, Pierre, was his nephew and had been in two nasty fights with the younger Briggs. But what Pierre didn't realize was that, in the first place, the trader had a good deal of respect for Jean Baptiste and knew he would do the best job of motivating and organizing the Indian trappers, and, secondly, he wanted him away from the post as much as possible because he knew if anyone would catch him in his underhanded business dealings it would be Jean Baptiste.

Pierre also noted with satisfaction that the younger Briggs kept about as far away from him as he could. He also noticed that the trader gave his son no job assignment. Pierre thought to himself, "No wonder he is so soft!"

As they left the stockade, Pierre asked his uncle, "Do you suppose we could bring Solomon with us?"

"That's a good idea, Pierre," Jean Baptiste responded, "But I'd better check with Briggs; I don't want to give him any excuse to complain. You wait here."

Jean Baptiste was back in a moment and reported with a grin, "I told Briggs Solomon could be an interpreter. He said he guessed it wouldn't do any harm. So—let's go find him."

Solomon proved easy to find; he had been sitting in the doorway of his uncle's cabin, waiting for the meeting to break up. Jean Baptiste let Pierre extend the invitation, and Solomon replied with an enthusiastic, "You bet your buttons!"—a phrase he had of course picked up from his father and his uncle.

The balance of the day was spent selecting and packing gifts and samples of trade goods that would be used to entice the Indians into hunting hard and bringing their furs to Turtle Portage, once the pelts were in prime—starting in the fall. In fact, some extra trade items would be taken along to exchange for the beaver fur robes the Indians had been wearing all winter. These brought a special premium price in Europe because they were worn with the fur on the inside, and the contact with the oils of the human skin gave the furs a special shine. The goods Jean Baptiste selected included cloth, beads, kettles, guns, powder, shot, awls (for working leather), twine (for making fish nets), knives, axe heads, and tobacco. Although rum and wine would be available for trade when the Indians brought their furs to the trading post, none was taken along on this excursion because Jean Baptiste knew that it could mean trouble. He knew from experience that the first village they would come to would want all they carried—now.

The next morning, two canoes with six passengers each and a supply of trade goods crossed Turtle Lake and then took a sharp left as they cleared the channel and entered Sabaskong Bay. The village they intended to visit was just a couple of miles up the shore.

Solomon told Pierre, "They know we come. Path through woods from trading post to village."

Solomon was right and most of the villagers were gathered on the shore as the canoes made their approach. Jean Baptiste and the other voyageurs were known to the villagers and there was a pleasant reunion.

Jean Baptiste distributed tobacco to everyone. Although Indians made their own from such plants as the red kinikinic, they prized more the black Brazilian tobacco carried by the French traders. He then made a little speech as he showed off each trade item. Although he knew enough of the language to get by, he let Solomon interpret. He ended by saying, "I will trade now for the beaver robes you wore last winter, and then if you will come to the trading post, we will give you more trading goods on credit against the furs you will trap this year."

The Indians shouted their approval and soon returned with their winter robes. A social time followed during which Solomon enjoyed showing off his new brother to his friends from the village.

Several Indians, however, approached Jean Baptiste to complain about the value trader Briggs placed on their furs. The voyageur promised to look into it, and made a mental note.

By nightfall they were back at the trading post with assurances for Briggs that the villagers were enthusiastic about trading and had promised to hunt and trap hard once the pelts were in prime.

The following morning, the canoes headed north into Whitefish Bay. Pierre noticed immediately how much clearer the water was than in Sabaskong Bay. Solomon explained, "Water deeper here than rest of lake. Shores rocky; not much dirt wash in when rains come. Fish different here, too. What you call 'trout' live on bottom—deep water."

Well before dark, their native guide had successfully pointed the way to a small village at a place the Indians called "Sioux Narrows," in remembrance of an unfriendly visit by a war party from that tribe. Here the ritual of the previous day was repeated, and Jean Baptiste again gave an enthusiastic sales pitch. Pierre expressed his surprise to his uncle that the Indians were invited to visit the trading post and select trade items on only a promise to pay for them with furs they had not yet trapped. Jean Baptiste explained, "This is a custom started on this lake by your great grandfather. It worked well for him and it works well for us. It builds a trust between the white man and the Indian. Our trading post will keep a separate record for each Indian. Of course if any trapper did not deliver his furs the next winter or spring, he would not be given credit the next year. The trader is careful too to not give more credit than the Indians are apt to make good for. In the spring, however, nearly every trapper has extra furs for still more trade goods. It's a good system; good for us and good for the Indians. The Hudson's Bay Company doesn't give credit and this gives us a real advantage."

The next stop was at a village site on Yellow Girl Point, just before leaving Whitefish Bay. From here, the canoes turned north and visited a large village where the waters of the Lake of the Woods dump into the Winnipeg River and flow all the way to Hudson Bay. The Indians named the area "Rat Portage," because muskrats often crossed there on their way to and from the sloughs just north of the lake. The voyageurs thought they might find evidence of the Hudson's Bay company here, but the Indians assured them the nearest port, to their knowledge, was on the Lake of Dirty Water (Winnipeg). Because Jean Baptiste was concerned the tribe might bring their furs to the rival company's posts to the north, he gave each an extra measure of tobacco and his very best sales pitch. He also gave them especially good exchange for their previous year's robes.

Next the voyageurs headed down the western arm of Lake of the Woods, finding few Indians until they were about halfway down the far shore. Here they found several small villages but were told there were some men from the Hudson's Bay Company on Buffalo Point. Jean Baptiste was not optimistic about luring the Indians to Turtle Portage with the rival operation so nearby, but he gave it his best try. He was also thinking of the future; he knew that if the Hudson's Bay operation proved temporary, these Indians could become good customers.

Before turning back east, Jean Baptiste told the boys, "We're going to take a day off and visit a very special place you've both heard a good deal about—your great-grandfather's old post, Fort St. Charles!"

Both boys expressed their pleasure and excitement and bombarded Jean Baptiste with questions—most of which he put off until they reached the site. He warned the boys, however, "There really isn't much left to see. The stockade has been pretty well broken down or burned and the same is true of the cabins. We think the Sioux did it."

Upon their arrival, the boys were thrilled to walk around the old fort. Pierre observed, "I feel like Moses did when God told him to take off his shoes because he was walking on holy ground."

As they explored, Jean Baptiste told how their great-grandfather (his grandfather), Pierre Gautherier De La Vérendrye, had been appointed by the Governor General of Canada, and that he and his four sons; Jean Baptiste, Pierre, Francois, and Louis-Joseph, had built seven forts, explored west as far as the mountains, discovered the legendary Mandan Indians with the European-like walled cities, and opened up trade with the Cree, Monsoni, and Assiniboin tribes.

"For many years," he told the boys, "this fort was the headquarters for all trade and exploration in the West."

He also told of the tragic massacre of the eldest son, Jean Baptiste, for whom he was named, Father Alneau (a young Catholic missionary), and nineteen soldiers and voyageurs.

"The remains of all twenty-one are buried here within the stockade," he told the boys.

As the stories of the La Vérendryes and their days of power and glory unfolded, Pierre couldn't help but ask, "What happened that our family no longer has power and wealth? Great-Grandfather was a captain in the service of the King of France; but neither you nor our father served in the military—how come?"

"You forget, Pierre," Jean Baptiste replied, "wars on far-off battlefields caused France to lose all of Canada to the British. Perhaps you will live to see the day when we are no longer second-class citizens, but, in the meantime, the most important positions are reserved for those of British ancestry. And as for wealth, your grandfather died a successful man, but not a wealthy man. Any money that was made went to his sponsors, the merchants of Montreal."

Solomon was a little baffled by all of this. He had heard some of the stories from his father but had not fully appreciated his French heritage. He observed, "Feel like two people—one French—other, Indian. Not know which me should be!"

"Just be yourself, Solomon," Jean Baptiste advised, "It is special to have two heritages—to enjoy two cultures. You are not two people; you are one person who is a blend of both."

"Sound good," Solomon replied, "Now tell—what big words say!"

On the journey east, the canoes paid a visit to two islands associated with the boys' ancestors. One was called "Corn Island" by the Indians (Garden Island by the whites). Pierre was amazed to find Indians farming on Lake of the Woods and growing such crops as corn, pumpkins, peas, and squash.

"Boys," Jean Baptiste explained, "It was your great-grandfather who taught the Indians of the lake how to farm and who gave them their first seeds."

The second island they visited was a relatively small outcropping, which Jean Baptiste approached almost with reverence as he explained, "This is where my uncle, Jean Baptiste, Father Alneau, and the others were murdered by the Sioux."

His description of the massacre and how legend had it that it was a sneak attack in which all of the whites were killed and most decapitated gave the boys goose bumps. He also spoke of how the bodies were decorated by the Indians with leg and arm bands made of porcupine quills.

"As the story goes," Jean Baptiste added, "a clap of thunder sounded when Father Alneau was killed and the war party fled in fear; they knew they had killed a Holy Man. One of the braves took the priest's altar and chalice and later, when back in his home village, gave the silver cup to his mother. Shortly after that, he and his brothers died violent deaths. The mother blamed this on the theft of the chalice and she threw it into the river on which their village was located."

"Wouldn't it be great," Pierre asked Solomon, "to find the silver chalice and give it to some church?"

Jean Baptiste reminded the boys that the river was probably in Sioux country and that it might not be a "healthy" quest even if they knew which river.

While on the southern part of the lake (called Lake of the Sandhills by the Indians), they visited another Indian village at the mouth of the Warroad River—so named, Jean Baptiste explained—because it was the route used by the Indians of the lake and the Indians of the plains as they waged war on one another. This was quite close to the Hudson's Bay operation, so little time was invested here. Then, on the way home, other Indians were visited on Big Island.

Two villages remained unvisited at the eastern end of Sabaskong Bay because the voyageurs had run out of gifts and trade items.

So, a few days later, the voyageurs were back at Turtle Portage reporting on their successful mission. Pierre had been particularly impressed by the huge size of Lake of the Woods, its seemingly countless islands (there are actually more than 14,000), and the great differences in appearance of the various parts of the lake. Solomon told him, "Indians say there four lakes—not one."

Pierre was impressed too with how the history of his family was so entwined with the history of this great body of water.

Perhaps most important, however, was the fact the trip had done much to help Solomon and Pierre become friends as well as brothers. On the evening of their return, as the boys sat by a fire and discussed their adventures, Pierre was very happy to hear Solomon say, "When first we meet—I hate you. Now—you bestest friend!"

CHAPTER IX
THE TURTLE PORTAGE POST

Upon returning to Turtle Portage after having visited Indian villages all around the lake, Pierre begged his brother to move in with him and Jean Baptiste. When the brothers had first met and their uncle had suggested they both share his cabin, Solomon was far from certain it would be a good idea, but he had become much better acquainted with Pierre during their travels and the hesitation he had felt earlier because of their first unpleasant encounter had vanished. And so it was that the two boys approached Winnetka and reminded her of Jean Baptiste's invitation. Solomon told his mother that he would like to give it a try. Winnetka, as would any mother in that situation, had mixed emotions. She loved her son very much and he was all she had left to remind her of her first husband. She feared too, that someday Solomon would want to become a part of the white man's world and moving out of her lodge might hasten that day. On the other hand, she recognized the importance of the brothers getting to know one another better before Pierre returned east. She knew too that their father would have wanted them together. "And after all," she told herself, "I do have my hands full with the young ones."

So in the end, Winnetka agreed to Solomon's leaving home—"Providing," she said, "you still help with the chores—like cutting fire wood. And promise to come home for meals once in awhile." And then added, in French, "You come too Pierre."

The boys were delighted and could not wait to tell Jean Baptiste. When they found him, he expressed his pleasure but cautioned Pierre, "Remember, you are a voyageur and you are expected to put in a full day's work for a full day's pay. You must not let the things you do with Solomon ever come before that obligation."

Pierre quickly agreed but asked, "Old Briggs won't mind if Solomon helps me once in awhile—for free, will he?"

"Well, that will probably depend on what it is, but we are not going to give him a chance to complain—understood?" Jean Baptiste answered and asked.

"Understood," Pierre agreed.

There was one structural change which took place in the voyageur's cabin shortly after Solomon moved in. Jean Baptiste returned home one night to find the boys building an interior wall, partitioning off about one-third of the cabin.

"What is going on here?" he demanded.

"Well," Pierre explained, "we thought you should have your own bedroom."

"Oh," Jean Baptiste responded, "that's thoughtful of you boys, thank you."

"Tell truth," Solomon urged Pierre with a big smile on his face.

"What's he talking about, Pierre?" Jean Baptiste wanted to know.

"Well, it's like this—" came the slow reply, "You snore too loud!"

Jean Baptiste tackled both boys in one swoop and a family free-for-all was the result—lasting until all three were too worn out from wrestling and laughing to carry on.

The last days of summer blended into fall as Pierre worked every day but Sunday—helping repair cabins, building a second store house, cutting fire wood, repairing the canoes, tending the gill nets for fish, and going with Jean Baptiste on a visit to the Indian villages they had been forced to skip the first trip around the lake. Once again, Solomon was given permission to join the crew as an interpreter, and the boys looked forward to their departure.

The voyageur's destination was, first, a village on the eastern end of Sabaskong Bay, just north of Nestor Falls, and second, a village which was actually located on another body of water, called "One-Sided Lake" (now known as Caliper Lake), which would be reached by a blazed trail through the woods.

They left on one of those early fall days which was so pleasant that you wished you could live forever. The birch and aspen were turning yellow and already a few fallen leaves spotted the dark rocks on the shore like pieces of gold. The bays of the lake were also yellow with heavy stands of wild rice; it was a good crop, more than the Indians could possibly harvest. A hard frost had cleared the lake of algae and the waters were once again sparkling clear. Even the sky seemed more blue.

The village on eastern Sabaskong Bay could easily have been reached in one day, but Jean Baptiste called a halt at Nestor Falls that first afternoon to let the men catch fish for supper. He chose this particular spot because it was known for the huge muskies and northern pike found there. Although they only had hand-lines and homemade metal spoons, the men caught far more fish than they could possibly eat and most were let go. Pierre and Solomon had a contest to see who could catch the biggest fish. Although each caught a muskie nearly as long as they were tall, they never did agree who won.

Solomon then challenged Pierre to see who could catch the first walleye—or "dore" as the French called them. Pierre wasn't sure how to fish them, but accepted the challenge anyway. Before he knew what to do, Solomon had caught a frog, put it on his hook, stepped out on a flat rock below the falls, and dropped it into a deep pool. In moments, the slack went out of his line. Minutes later, a huge walleye—at least ten pounds—came flopping out on the rock.

"All right, Pierre," Solomon teased, "now who best fisherman?"

"Now who best wrestler?" Pierre teased back as he tackled his brother and the two went head-over-heels down a slope into a patch of grass, where Pierre, as usual, emerged the victor—but not without working hard. Solomon's long legs were forever giving Pierre trouble as he entwined them around his mid-section and squeezed unmercifully. His only defense was to get hold of one of Solomon's feet and twist until he forced his legs apart. Pierre was thankful for all those workouts with Jean Baptiste the previous winter and wasn't about to share any of what he had learned with his brother.

The next day at the Indian village, Jean Baptiste once again distributed gifts of tobacco, showed off the trade items, and gave his best sales talk. This was all repeated at the village on beautiful One-Sided Lake. In both cases, the Indians promised to bring their furs to Turtle Portage, but not without complaining that trader Briggs did not give them full value for their furs—compared to what they had received at the Hudson's Bay post when it was located at the mouth of the Rainy River.

Jean Baptiste reminded them how far they would now have to go to trade with the Hudson's Bay people, but again made a mental note of the complaint.

On the way home, the voyageurs decided to do a little meat hunting. Jean Baptiste's crew concentrated on big game, while the second canoe hunted ducks, pigeons, and partridges.

Since Pierre had never shot a moose, he was to be given the first chance. The next morning before daybreak, when one could just barely make things out in the false dawn, Jean Baptiste, Angel, and the two boys paddled out of camp. Their target was Split Rock Bay. Pierre sat in the bow and when they reached the mouth of the bay where they had a good view of the shallow feeding areas and Jean Baptiste had sig-nalled a stop, he positioned his uncle's muzzleloader across his knees. There, they waited in complete silence. Pierre marveled at all the noises he heard as the wilderness came to life: songbirds chirping, ducks quacking, crows cawing, and partridges clucking as they prepared to fly down from their roosts in the aspens. Far back in the forest he heard the almost human cry of a lynx. Out on the main lake, loons talked to each other, their voices carrying for miles on the still morning air. Then he heard it—"u-u-u-u-uh!"—the unmistakable grunt of a moose. It was followed by twigs and branches snapping and slapping against the animal's heavy hide as it made its way towards the lake. It seemed forever, but actually in a matter of a few minutes a huge bull with antlers that looked five feet across stepped out of the shore brush and into the water. It casually waded out to shoulder depth and then began to feed on bottom vegetation. On a signal from Jean Baptiste, the men made their move—paddling without ever lifting their paddles out of the water. The canoe glided forward in total silence. The huge animal just went on feeding—plunging his entire head under water. Once he came up with a long lily pad plant draped from his antlers. Pierre wanted to laugh but settled for a smile. Closer and closer they paddled. The moose loomed so large he just knew he couldn't miss—even now—but Pierre waited for his uncle's signal. When less than 100 feet remained, the moose dipped his head under water once again, and Jean Baptiste whispered, "When he comes up, let him have it, in the chest."

Pierre raised the heavy muzzleloader. He couldn't believe how long the moose held its breath. The barrel began to wave back and forth and up and down. Pierre was shaking. Then the gigantic head came up, water cascading from the antlers! Pierre found the front bead in the groove of the rear site and moved it, still shaking, onto the enormous chest and then squeezed the trigger. Ker pow!! The moose raised up on its hind legs and then crashed to one side with a loud splash—very much dead.

"Good shot!" Solomon yelled.

Then the work began. The four had all they could to to manhandle the more than half-ton of dead weight to shore, where they could more

Then the giant head came up, water cascading from its antlers.

easily proceed with the butchering. While they worked, Angel asked, "Did anyone else feel the canoe vibrating while we were waiting for Pierre to shoot?"

Jean Baptiste and Solomon acknowledged that they did, the latter adding, "That just scared Pierre shaking!"

But Angel observed, "I don't think just one person could cause that much vibration. I think we were all pretty excited."

As they loaded the meat into the canoe, Pierre asked, "Why didn't the moose run when we came so close?"

Jean Baptiste answered, "For some reason animals are much less afraid when approached on water. They must instinctively feel nothing can harm them out on the lake. Then too," he added, "I was very careful to keep our faces into the breeze so he couldn't smell us."

When they returned to their campsite they learned that the other canoe had been equally successful in hunting small game, and the expedition returned to Turtle Portage in triumph.

The next Sunday, which the boys had off, they agreed to try their hand at duck hunting in the rice bed across Turtle Lake. Since the muzzleloaders could shoot only a single shot without reloading, it took most of the day to collect a respectable bag of ducks, even though the northern flight was on and mallards kept pouring into the rice bed from the north. Both boys had great difficulty hitting anything in the air and had most of their success on the water—usually trying to line up more than one bird at a time. Solomon had the record for the day—three big "green heads" in one shot.

The following Sunday, they went after bluebills on the open waters of Sabaskong Bay. Huge rafts of the diving birds usually sat pretty tight until the canoe was within at least long range. Again, whoever was in the front of the canoe tried to line up as many ducks as he could for that one shot. The boys noticed a low narrows midway on a long island where the bluebills flew across quite low in "bundles." They decided it would be fun to see if they could connect in the air. Pierre discovered he was not leading the ducks far enough when he finally dropped one and it was the third bird behind the duck he was shooting at! But even when the boys had learned how to lead them, they still connected on only about one in four tries.

The autumn days grew shorter and colder, and finally the brothers awoke one morning to find Turtle Lake completely frozen. The White Fish Bay side of the portage stayed open a couple of weeks longer—since it was so much deeper. But the approaching winter finally won that victory too.

One Sunday when the ice was not yet safe for walking, the boys followed the well-worn path through the woods from Turtle Portage to the Indian village on Sabaskong Bay. Solomon had several friends there, including a pretty girl about his own age, called "O-gay-bow." Pierre teased Solomon so much about his "girl friend," he didn't dare show any particular interest himself in any of the other girls!

When the snows came to stay, it signalled the time to use the sled dogs for transportation. Each family at Turtle Portage had a team—usually five in number—and there were other teams available to the voyageurs. With most of the work done around the post, the Frenchmen were free to hunt and trap. They were paid for their services so they did not receive the same return on their furs as did the Indians, but they were allowed to trade for goods or receive extra money if they went beyond their quota. They respected the traplines laid out by the Indians and usually ventured out farther from the post, sometimes staying overnight in a "spike camp," which was just a small lodge which provided shelter against the wind and the cold. Pierre was allowed to hunt with Solomon because he was his brother. The boys worked hard and did well enough so that Pierre more than met his quota as a voyageur and by winter's end had enough extra pelts to pay for the muzzleloader he had purchased on credit.

Pierre noticed that young Jonathan Briggs was almost always alone, except when he was with his father. He actually felt sorry for him and even suggested to Solomon, "Maybe we should take Jonathan with us sometime."

But Solomon's sharp reply discouraged any such idea, "Him no good. He always push me around last year. Only leave me alone 'cause you here!"

While on the trapline one day, Pierre had his first opportunity to shoot a caribou. It was late in the afternoon and the boys were on their way back to Turtle Portage. They were just about to take the portage route from Sabaskong Bay around the thinly covered channel into Turtle Lake, when they spotted a herd of a dozen or more animals crossing the ice between the peninsula and Hay Island. Pierre sat in the toboggan, gun ready, while Solomon stood on the rear runners of the sled and drove his dogs. Although the caribou moved at a surprisingly fast trot, the boys soon pulled alongside the herd and Pierre dropped a nice bull at point-blank range. Because the winter was nearly over, the animal had long since shed its antlers—but that mattered little to the boys; they were only interested in the tasty meat, which they proudly brought back to camp.

As the winter warmed to spring, the snow on the lake melted first, and then the ice turned dark and began to crystallize. The voyageurs knew there would soon be open water and the trading post would be over-run with Indian trappers—whole families—bringing in the fruits of their winter's labors. These would indeed be busy days, with the post open for business from sunrise to sunset.

As the boys sat visiting one evening, Pierre spoke of the coming spring. "I'm anxious for ice-out," he said. "Once the trading is done we'll be starting back for Rainy Lake, and then there'll be the big Rendez-vous at Grand Portage, and then, when that's done, we'll be heading home."

"Can't hardly wait, huh?" Solomon asked.

"Well, not really," Pierre replied, and then continued, "but it will be good to be back in the canoe with the other voyageurs, paddling and singing as we go among the islands and up the rivers. And when we get to Grand Portage, the Rendezvous will be terribly exciting."

"Then why you not glad you go home?" Solomon asked, testingly.

"Well," Pierre began, and then fell silent—scratching in some dirt on the ground recently left bare by the melting snow.

"Well, what?" Solomon finally asked.

"Well," Pierre repeated, "there's nobody at home my age. We live quite a ways out in the bush and there's no one around. Oh, you know how much I love Uncle Jean and what great fun it is to be with him—and Aunt Emile is just super—but—well," Pierre stared at the ground, "well, I'm going to miss you."

Pierre couldn't believe he had said it, but it was the truth.

Both boys were silent for awhile, then Solomon acknowledge, "Me miss Pierre too."

CHAPTER X
CAUGHT IN THE ACT

Ice-out came early on Lake of the Woods in the year of 1794. During the first week of April, open veins of water appeared on Turtle Lake; by mid-month, the ice was out of Sabaskong Bay; and on the last weekend, all that remained of the signs of winter on Whitefish Bay were a few shifting rafts of ice. With the lake open, Indian families began converging on the Turtle Portage post, their canoes heaped with prime furs. Canoe loads of trade goods from the Rainy Lake port had filled the stockade storehouse the previous summer, but Pierre wondered if the building could possibly hold enough things to satisfy the Indian's desires to barter for goods beyond the credit which had been given the previous fall. Not only had the Indian men hunted and trapped, but so had the women—and even the children. Trader Briggs was in his glory. He did allow some of the voyageurs to assist him by trading for the less valuable furs like muskrat, raccoon, red fox, and wolf. But he personally handled the more valuable pelts, including lynx, beaver, fisher, cross and silver fox, marten, and mink. During the early weeks of May, he sat at the trading table from sunup to sundown, and sometimes into the night. Since Turtle Portage was a small post, it did not have a fur press, so pelts of each variety were simply tied in bundles. Pierre was one of the voyageurs assigned this task.

Rum was a favorite trade item, and, unfortunately, it was one of the first things many Indians asked for. Once they had consumed more than they could handle, they were fair game for Jonathan Briggs. Not only did he give them less than fair value for their furs, but if they were really drunk and didn't know what they were doing, he would give them little or nothing—except possibly a few more drinks. When they sobered up and asked where the goods were they had gotten for their furs, he told them they had chosen to drink up all they had coming. For-

Trading goods from the voyageurs' packs.   Courtesy Minnesota Historical Society

tunately, most had received goods on credit the previous fall or they would have had nothing to show for their winter's labor but a hangover.

Since Jean Baptiste had been warned by George Mc Kay, the Rainy River factor, that Briggs might be cheating the Indians and since wherever he had been on the Lake of the Woods the previous autumn he had heard the Indians' complaints of too few goods for their furs, he positioned himself where he could watch the trader operate firsthand. It didn't take long to convince him that Briggs was collecting far more furs than he should for the trade items given in return—especially from those who were drunk. The big question was, what would happen to the extra furs? Mc Kay had told him that last year the books had balanced—trade goods for furs. Jean Baptiste confided to his nephews, "Either Briggs will be turning in too many furs at Rainy Lake, or he will be getting rid of the surplus. My guess is that somehow—some way— he will hide them for some woods runner (the French called them 'coureurs de bois') to pick up and sell back East—then they'll divide the profit."

"What's a woods runner?" Solomon asked.

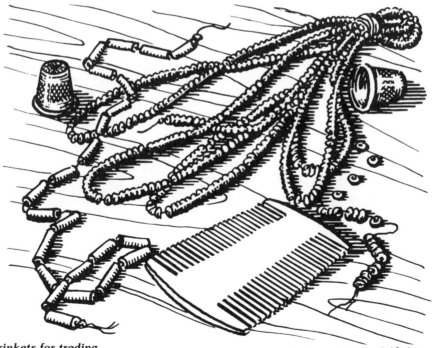

Trinkets for trading.

Courtesy Minnesota Historical Society

"Well," Jean Baptiste explained, "All voyageurs and traders are licensed by the government so that there is some control of the fur trading business. But some men choose to operate illegally or have lost their license. If they are caught, they will probably go to prison. They make their money by visiting out-of-the-way Indian villages and then selling the furs to crooked merchants. Anyway, we call them "woods runners.""

"I'd love to catch old Briggs hiding furs!" Pierre said, gleefully rubbing his hands together in anticipation of such an exciting possibility.

"Let's you and me watch him, Pierre," Solomon suggested.

"That's exactly what I wanted to talk to you boys about," Jean Baptiste broke in. "But you'll have to be very careful—he's a sly one. And it could be dangerous—he would rather kill than be caught."

And so the Pierre-Solomon spy operation began.

"We watch young Briggs too. Him crook too," Solomon suggested.

"Ya, they're no doubt in it together," Pierre agreed.

Jean Baptiste pointed out that Briggs would probably not make his move until there were fewer people around—after the Indians had returned to their villages. "Until then," he said, "you boys can relax, but it wouldn't hurt to keep an eye on them."

The boys were so excited, however, at the prospect of catching the pompous Briggs in the act of stealing, that one or the other of them was in a position to keep track of the activities of both the trader and his son from that point on. Actually, it was only a few days later that the last of the visiting Indian families departed for their home villages and Turtle Portage was restored to peaceful inactivity. That very same day, Jean Baptiste sat down with his nephews to plan their surveillance. He was in the middle of explaining his plan for a night watch when there was a knock on their cabin door. Pierre opened it to reveal none other than the smiling face of Jonathan Briggs, Sr.

"Uh, come in—sir," Pierre stammered.

"No—that's all right," the trader responded as he spotted Jean Baptiste. "I just wanted to announce a celebration! Trading has been so good I'm throwing a party tonight for the voyageurs and the Indian families who live here at the portage. So, I'd appreciate it if you would spread the word. And Solomon, be sure to tell the Indian folks they're invited too."

As he left, the La Vérendryes stared at each other in disbelief. They had never seen Briggs so cheerful and friendly.

"This is it!" Jean Baptiste blurted out, "He'll get everybody drunk and then make his move."

"So what'll we do?" Pierre asked eagerly.

"I'll tell you what we won't do—we won't get drunk," Jean Baptiste replied. "But I want you to act like you are—and then slip away from the party like you've had too much and gotten sick. But if either of you take one sip—I'll kill you! Understand?"

The boys nodded their understanding, but Pierre added, "Huh, you wouldn't let us drink even if we didn't have to keep alert!"

"You got that right," Jean Baptiste admitted, and then went on, "You boys will take the first watch after the party is over. You can keep each other awake. But when you get sleepy, one of you can slip back here and wake me up and then I'll finish out the night. And if they make a move, come and get me. Don't even think of acting on your own."

The party began with a big feast; the cook really outdid himself. It featured roast beaver, venison, and moose—and plenty for all. Briggs broke out kegs of high wine and rum and uncharacteristically urged everyone to eat and drink their fill. Even young Briggs seemed to catch the spirit and sought out Pierre and Solomon and suggested, "Let's let bygones be bygones. It's time we became friends."

Pierre and Solomon went along with it, the former responding, "It's too bad we had those fights last summer; we could have had good times together all along."

And Solomon added, "You pretty good guy after all."

After Jonathan had left, Solomon teased, "Not nice to lie!"

Both boys pretended to have been drinking—Jean Baptiste told them later they would make good professional actors—and slipped away, feigning illness, when the party was still in full swing. With Briggs' encouragement, it didn't take long to get everyone drunk. By dark, all had either gone home or passed out. Jean Baptiste made sure he was the last to leave, and then staggered back to the cabin. Here he met the boys as prearranged.

"All right, you have the first watch. Stay together, keep quiet, and come back to me if you see anything suspicious," Jean Baptiste counseled.

With that, the boys slipped out into the night. There was a full moon just coming up over Whitefish Bay; it would make it easier to keep watch. Pierre and Solomon were about to climb a pine—which they had preselected—overlooking the stockade area, but they never had a chance to take their perch. As Solomon was about to give his brother a boost, the boys heard the stockade gate creak open and recognized the muffled voices of the trader and his son. The brothers stepped into the shadows and squatted motionless.

Briggs, senior and junior, walked within a few feet of them as they headed for the Whitefish Bay side of the isthmus—each struggling with two huge bundles of furs. The younger Briggs grunted, "I'm glad this is the last load—Gerard had better be at the island after all this work."

"He'll be there, all right," the father responded. "And stop complaining; the cash that'll be waiting for us in Montreal will make it all worthwhile and then some."

"They must have worked fast," Pierre whispered. "We'd better not lose sight of them."

Noiselessly, the boys followed in the shadows—about twenty yards behind. When they reached the height of ground between the two bodies of water, they could make out a beached canoe, silhouetted against the reflection of the moonlight on the water.

"They get away!" Solomon whispered. "Better get Uncle Jean!"

"There's no time," Pierre replied. "You and I have got to stop them now. I'll take the old man; you take the kid."

"I don't know if we can," Solomon whispered back. "Him a man, and boy beat me up bad last year."

"Sure we can," Pierre insisted. "Let me worry about the old man; he's so fat he'll be a pushover. We'll surprise them; we'll have the advantage. When you tackle Jonathan, wrap those long legs of yours around his belly and squeeze. If you can get behind him or alongside him, pull up under his armpits and push down with your legs—and then turn your knees into his stomach and backbone. Let out a warwhoop as you hit him. Let's go!"

The Briggs' were nearly to their canoe when Pierre and Solomon let out their bloodthirsty yells as they tackled them from behind. Two of the bundles broke open and the night was suddenly filled with flying furs and tumbling bodies.

The attack caught trader and son by complete surprise and both went down in shock—hard. Briggs, Senior fell flat on his face and Pierre was on his back in a flash. Young Briggs landed more on his side with Solomon on top. He was the first to recognize the attackers and shouted to his father, "It's only Pierre and Solomon—no problem!"

But Solomon had a plan and quickly rolled the fat boy all the way over, locking his legs around his stomach as they rolled. Young Briggs ended up on his back with Solomon locked to his side—pushing down with his legs and pulling up under the left arm—just as Pierre had coached. In a matter of seconds he was in complete control with his opponent gasping for breath and squealing in real pain whenever Solomon applied pressure. Every time young Jonathan tried to break loose, Solomon pulled up with his arms, squeezed and pushed down with his legs, and turned his knobby knees into his adversary's backbone and soft belly.

Pierre, however, was having much greater difficulty. Trader Briggs was a big man and under all that fat there was a good deal of mature strength. Starting flat on his face, he slowly but deliberately worked himself up to his knees and then stood up, as though the boy on his back were weightless. Pierre quickly jumped off and tackled the man from the side. He caught Briggs off balance once again, and again he went down in a heap. But before Pierre could turn him over onto his back, he rolled to his knees and once more got to his feet—shaking off Pierre like a dog would shake water off its fur after being in a lake. Pierre knew he had to get the big man down on his back, so this time he attacked from the front, went down on one knee. grasped Briggs around his thick legs, and tried to lift him off the ground, but found he couldn't!

Briggs wheezed his first words, "Is this what you are trying to do?"

And he effortlessly picked Pierre off the ground and lifted him high in the air, squeezing him around the waist with all his might in a bear hug. Pierre could scarcely breathe and struggled in vain to get loose.

"All right, young man," Briggs snorted, "I'm taking you to your uncle and charging you with fur theft!"

With that, he started walking back towards the fort, with Pierre's arms and legs helplessly flailing the air.

Jean Baptiste had taught Pierre to think when he wrestled, and the boy finally did just that—recalling the countermove his uncle had taught him. He raised his hands high above his head and then brought them down with all his strength—on edge—on the man's tender collar bones. Briggs screamed out in genuine pain and let go.

Pierre quickly went on the offensive once again. This time he picked up just one of Briggs' legs, tipping him off balance and dropped him to the ground. Briggs lit on his back and Pierre flopped on top—across his chest. His legs quickly found one arm and encircled it like a scissors. With his two arms he was able to gain control of Briggs' left wrist and hold it against the ground. Briggs tried to buck and kick but his overweight condition quickly took its toll and he was soon out of both breath and strength.

Pierre, for the first time, had the opportunity to check on his brother and asked, "How are you doing, Solomon?"

"Lots better than you!" came the reply. "No problem!"

Solomon gave young Jonathan a squeeze with his legs just to make him bellow.

"What do now?" Solomon asked.

"Yell like crazy!" came the reply.

And both boys began screaming, "Uncle Jean! Uncle Jean!"

The cabin was less than 100 yards away and Jean Baptiste, who was just dozing off, heard and bounded to his feet with a start. He threw open the door and yelled, "I'm coming!"

With the help of the full moon and guided by the shouts of his nephews, he had no trouble finding the "battle ground."

When the boys saw their uncle they began yelling, "We caught them! We caught them both! They were putting furs into a canoe!"

Briggs argued back, "They lie! We caught *them* stealing furs."

Jean Baptiste dismissed the trader's charges by saying, "I know better. Even Mc Kay knew you were up to something and asked me to keep an eye on you."

Angel and the Maiden shared a cabin next to the La Vérendrye's and, although still a bit tipsy, heard the commotion and at this point came upon the scene. Jean Baptiste quickly explained what had happened and in minutes ropes were found and the crooked trader and his son were both bound hand and foot. By this time the whole camp was aroused. Pierre and Solomon were instant heroes—no one liked the trader or his son.

Torches were lit and Jean Baptiste began his interrogation: "Where were you taking those furs?"

"We were going to hide them," Briggs replied matter-of-factly.

"No they weren't!" Pierre spoke up. "I heard Jonathan say he hoped someone named 'Gerard' would be at some island to meet them."

Holding a torch in one hand and grabbing Briggs by the throat with the other, Jean Baptiste looked him straight in the eye—nose to nose—and said, "If you cooperate and are real helpful, I will tell Mc Kay and he *may* go easier on you."

Briggs was silent for a minute, obviously contemplating his fate, and then responded, "We were to meet a coureurs de bois (woods runner) on the island in front of Devil's Bay."

Briggs was telling the truth, he had chosen this particular island because most Indians believed the bay to be haunted by wendigoes (evil spirits) and, therefore, weren't likely to be around at night and see what was going on.

"What signal were you to give this Gerard as you approached?" Jean Baptiste wanted to know.

Before Briggs could answer, Angel added, "Tell the truth because if anything goes wrong and Jean Baptiste does not return, we will kill you at daybreak!"

Briggs quickly replied, "I was to make the sound of a loon and Gerard would answer with an owl call if everything was all right."

Satisfied that he was telling the truth, Jean Baptiste chose the Maiden to accompany him in one canoe and selected two of the more sober voyageurs to follow in a second as a back-up in case of trouble.

Pierre begged, "Let us go!"

But Jean Baptiste shook his head, "No, you've done more than enough. Besides, there may be shooting."

Although they were gone less than three hours, it seemed like an eternity to Pierre and Solomon. But just as it was starting to get light, the boys were able to make out the canoes returning in the distance. As they drew closer, they could see a third man in the first canoe. It was the one called Gerard, and he had been tied as securely as the trader and his son.

The boys bombarded Jean Baptiste with questions, but his report was short: "It went well. Gerard answered my loon call and when he stepped out into the open to catch our canoe, I pointed the muzzle-loader in his face and ordered him to put his hands above his head and stand very still—and he did. That was all there was to it."

Pierre and Solomon were allowed to travel with the voyageurs who took the captives to the Rainy Lake post. Jean Baptiste let the boys tell Chief Trader Mc Kay their part of the story. They were real heroes.

As for the Briggs', they had little to say. Mc Kay expressed his bitter disappointment to the father and added, "Of course, you will be returned to Montreal along with this woods runner to stand trial."

He then put Jean Baptiste in charge of the Turtle Lake post as the voyageurs closed out the operation there for another year.

The boys were honored guests at dinner that night, and Pierre sat to Mc Kay's left and Solomon to his right. At the end of the evening, the Chief Trader urged Pierre, "Go back to school. Take mathematics and astronomy and learn how to survey. There is room for a young man like you in our company. I will speak a good word for you when the time comes."

And to Solomon he added, "You lack your brother's education, but I'm sure you would learn quickly. Why don't you return East with him and learn to read and write. With your knowledge of the Indian languages you could also have a good job with us."

After returning to Turtle Portage, the boys talked much of Mc Kay's offer and advice and Pierre begged his brother to return home with him, but Solomon insisted he belonged in the wilderness.

An interesting aftermath of the boys' capture of Briggs and son came when Solomon and Pierre had their next friendly wrestling match. It seems Pierre's coaching was a little too good; he had made the mistake of sharing what Jean Baptiste had taught him when he advised his brother how to handle young Briggs. Even though it was just one hold, guess who won the match? You're right—Solomon! The scissors, applied with his brother's long legs, had always given Pierre trouble, and when Solomon added the body stretch and turned his knees into Pierre's back and stomach, and when Pierre couldn't quite get hold of Solomon's foot to break the hold, it was a little too much. Chalk one up for Solomon!

The day came all too quickly when the voyageurs would have to leave. Pierre and Solomon had avoided talking about their separation; each dreaded it too much.

The canoes were loaded and lined up on the beach for departure, but Solomon was nowhere to be seen—in fact, he hadn't been around all morning. Pierre searched the fort and the cabins; he just couldn't leave without saying "good-bye" to his brother. It would be more than a year before he would see him again. Finally, he concluded Solomon couldn't bear seeing him leave so he gave up the search; he knew he had been delaying the voyageurs' departure. Sadly he walked to his canoe and helped shove off. He said nothing as they paddled across Turtle Lake. When his uncle broke into song, he just couldn't join in.

About the time they entered the channel, he noticed a voyageur two places in front of him had on some of his own clothes! From the back it looked like—but it just couldn't be—it looked like his brother. Unbelievingly, hesitantly, he lifted his paddle and with it touched the voyageur's shoulder.

Slowly, the voyageur turned around.

It was Solomon—grinning from ear to ear!